HODDER

mathematics

FOUNDATION

1

Series editor: Roger Porkess

Catherine Berry
Dave Faulkner
Geoff Rigby
John Spencer

Hodder & Stoughton

A MEMBER OF THE HODDER HEADLINE GROUP

Acknowledgements

The authors and publishers would like to thank the following companies, institutions and individuals who have given permission to reproduce copyright material: RAC, Our Price, NatWest, McDonald's, The Royal Bank of Scotland and Ordnance Survey. The publishers will be happy to make arrangements with any copyright holders whom it has not been possible to contact.

Illustrations were drawn by Ian Foulis and Associates, Maggie Brand, Bill Donohoe, Tony Wilkins and Ann Kronheimer.

Photos supplied by Hulton Getty (pages 16 and 188), Hodder Picture Library (page 81).

Page design and cover design by Lynda King.

Orders: please contact Bookpoint Ltd, 39 Milton Park, Abingdon, Oxon OX14 4TD.
Telephone: (44) 01235 400414, Fax: (44) 01235 400454. Lines are open from 9.00 – 6.00,
Monday to Saturday, with a 24 hour message answering service. Email address: orders@bookpoint.co.uk

British Library Cataloguing in Publication Data

A catalogue record for this title is available from The British Library

ISBN 0 340 705 485

First published 1998
Impression number   10 9 8 7 6 5 4 3 2 1
Year   2004 2003 2002 2001 2000 1999 1998

Cover photo from Science Photo Library

Typeset by Multiplex Techniques Ltd, Orpington, Kent.

Printed in Hong Kong for Hodder & Stoughton Educational, a division of Hodder Headline Plc, 338 Euston Road, London NW1 3BH by Colorcraft Ltd.

Introduction

This is the first of two textbooks covering Foundation Tier GCSE. Students following a two year course would expect to take one year on each book, those on a one year course half that time. The books cover the requirements of Foundation Tier GCSE and so are suitable for use with any syllabus. The division of material between them is made on the basis of the modules within the MEI syllabus. They also cover the mathematics requirements of GNVQ Application of Number at Levels 1 and 2.

This book is divided into 21 chapters, forming a logical progression through the material (some teachers may however wish to vary this order). Each chapter is divided into a number of double-page spreads, designed to be teaching units. The material to be taught is covered on the left-hand page; the right-hand pages consist entirely of work for the students to do. Each chapter ends with a mixed exercise covering all of its content. Further work sheets and tests are provided in the Teacher's Resource.

The instruction (i.e. left-hand) pages have been designed to help teachers engage their students in whole class discussion. The symbol ⏱ is used to indicate a discussion point; teachers should see it as an invitation.

Each of the right-hand pages ends with a practical activity. These are suitable for both GCSE and GNVQ students; some can be used for portfolio tasks. Advice on these is available in the Teacher's Resource and, where relevant, data is also supplied. Most students will not do all of the activities (they are quite time-consuming) but the authors think it is important that they do some of them in order to connect the mathematics classroom to the outside world and to other subjects.

Where knowledge is assumed, this is stated at the start of the chapter, but in addition, there is a general expectation that students will know the four rules of basic arithmetic and be able to carry out simple long multiplication and division. Questions are expected to be answered without the use of a calculator (except for checking), unless the calculator icon ▦ indicates otherwise.

Although students are to be encouraged to use I.T., particularly spreadsheets, specific guidance is limited to the Teacher's Resource. Otherwise, the book would have been based on one particular package to the frustration of those using all the others.

The authors would like to thank those who helped in preparing this book, particularly Geoff Dunn and Julian Thomas for their advice on early versions of the manuscript, and Karen Eccles who has typed many a page.

Contents

Contents

How to use this book

This symbol next to a question means you are allowed to use your calculator. Don't use your calculator if you can't see the symbol!

This symbol means you will need to think carefully about a point. Your teacher may ask you to join in a discussion about it.

Angles

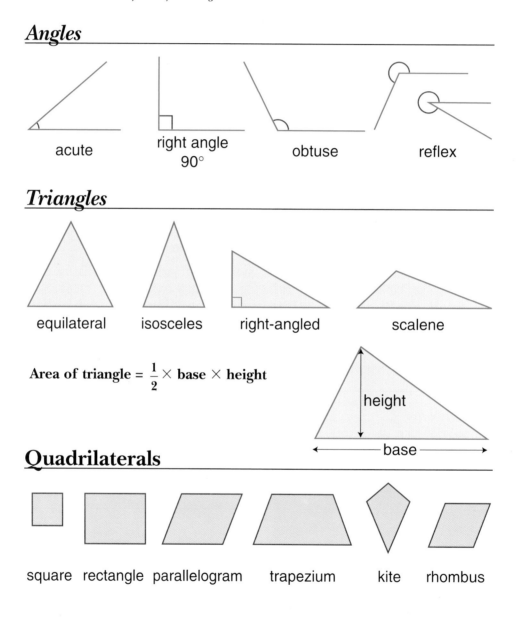

acute   right angle 90°   obtuse   reflex

Triangles

equilateral   isosceles   right-angled   scalene

Area of triangle = $\frac{1}{2} \times$ base $\times$ height

height

base

Quadrilaterals

square   rectangle   parallelogram   trapezium   kite   rhombus

Circles

Circumference of circle $= \pi \times$ diameter
$\qquad\qquad\qquad = 2 \times \pi \times$ radius

Area of circle $= \pi \times (\text{radius})^2$

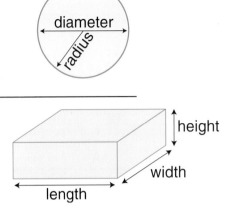

Solid figures

Volume of cuboid = length $\times$ width $\times$ height

Units

Metric system

Length
1000 metres = 1 kilometre
1000 millimetres = 1 metre

100 centimetres = 1 metre
10 millimetres = 1 centimetre

Mass
1000 grams = 1 kilogram
1000 milligrams = 1 gram

Capacity
1000 litres = 1 kilolitre
1000 millilitres = 1 litre

kilo = 1000 times

centi = $\dfrac{1}{100}$ times

milli = $\dfrac{1}{1000}$ times

Approximate conversions

1 km = $\dfrac{5}{8}$ miles

1 m = 39.37 inches

1 kg = 2.2 pounds (lb)

1 litre = $1\dfrac{3}{4}$ pints

1 foot = 30.5 cm

1 inch = 25.4 mm

1 pound = 454 g

1 gallon = 4.5 litres

Long multiplication and long division examples

434×14

```
  434
   14
————
 4340
 1736
————
 6076
```

Answer: 6067

$434 \div 14$

```
        31
    ————
14) 434
     42
    ————
     14
     14
    ————
    ..
    ——
```

Answer: 31

One

Co-ordinates

Finding a square

You are visiting the city of York.

Here is a street map to help you find your way around.

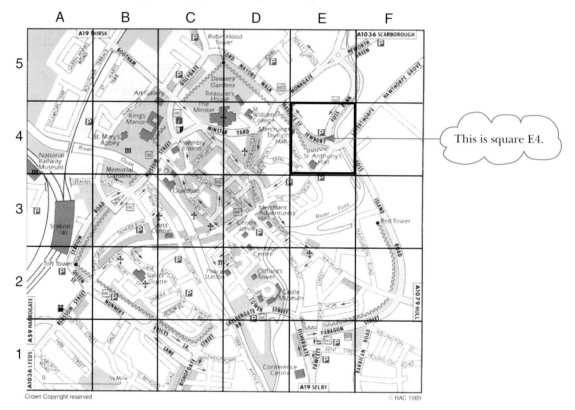

This is square E4.

Find Centre Jorvik.

Find the Police Station.

Unless you already know York, it's like looking for a needle in a haystack, isn't it?

The square grid is there to help you. Each square has a number and a letter.

Find these places.

- *The Sports Centre in square* B2
- *Tower Street in square* D2
- *St Mary's Abbey in square* B4

You can see that it is easier to find things when you know which square to look in.

1 Look at the map of York city centre.
In which square is
a) Clifford's Tower?
b) the Railway Station?
c) the Red Tower?

2 Look at this plan of Castle Bromwich Gardens.
In which square (or squares) is
a) the South Gate?
b) the West pond?
c) the New orchard?
d) the maze?

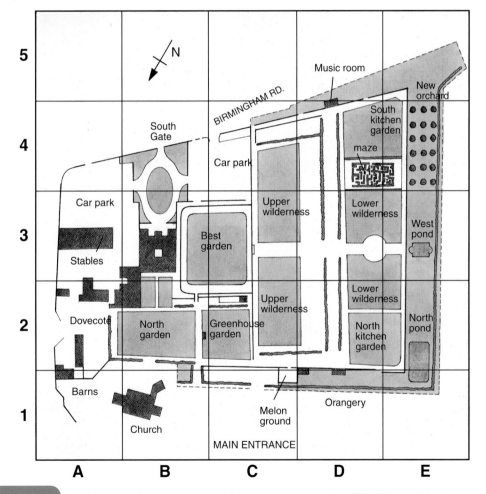

Airline seats often have a number (to tell you the row) and a letter (to tell you the seat). So 4H means row 4, seat H.

Make a list of other places in which a letter and a number are used to locate something.

How does this kind of system help?

Finding a point

Sue is a landscape gardener.
She is planning the Smiths' garden.
She draws this plan. The distances are in metres.

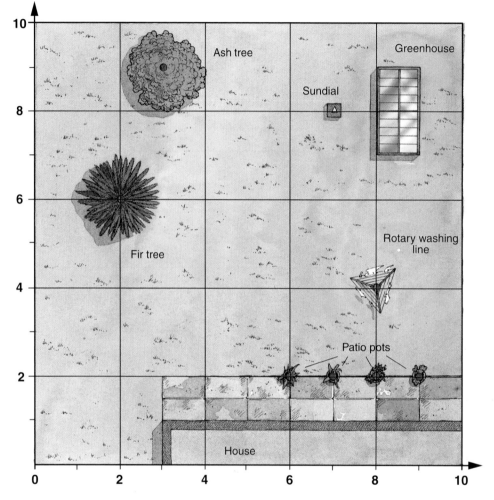

Sue has marked the positions of the trees.
She has used **co-ordinates**.

The fir tree is at (2,6).
The first number, 2, tells you the distance across the garden.
The second number, 6, tells you the distance along the garden.

Using co-ordinates you can describe exactly where things are.

The ash tree is at (3,9).
How far is it from the left hand side of the garden?

What are the co-ordinates of the washing line?

Where is the point (0,0)?

Sue's assistant plants the fir tree at (6,2) instead of (2,6).
Where does she plant it?

The owner puts a garden gnome at $(3,1\frac{1}{2})$.
Describe its position.

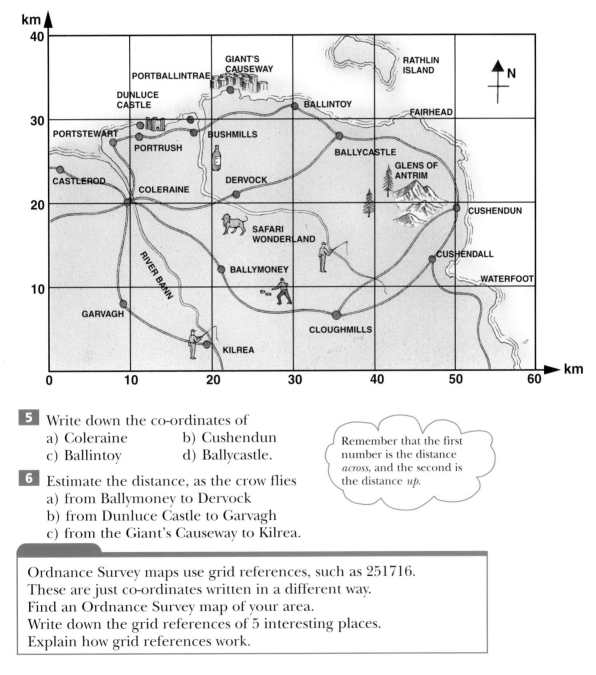

Exercise

Look again at Sue's plan.

1 What are the co-ordinates of the sundial?

2 What are the co-ordinates of the patio pots?
(There are 4 pots so you need 4 sets of co-ordinates.)

3 How far is the sundial from the side of the greenhouse?

4 How wide and how long are the patio slabs?

Look at this map of the Causeway Coast in Northern Ireland.
The distances are in kilometres.

5 Write down the co-ordinates of
a) Coleraine   b) Cushendun
c) Ballintoy   d) Ballycastle.

Remember that the first number is the distance *across*, and the second is the distance *up*.

6 Estimate the distance, as the crow flies
a) from Ballymoney to Dervock
b) from Dunluce Castle to Garvagh
c) from the Giant's Causeway to Kilrea.

Ordnance Survey maps use grid references, such as 251716.
These are just co-ordinates written in a different way.
Find an Ordnance Survey map of your area.
Write down the grid references of 5 interesting places.
Explain how grid references work.

Mathematical co-ordinates

You have seen how a square grid can be used to locate an area or a point on a map or plan.

You can also use a square grid in mathematics.

You draw and label a pair of **axes**. (It is easiest to do this on graph paper.)

You can identify any point on the grid using co-ordinates.

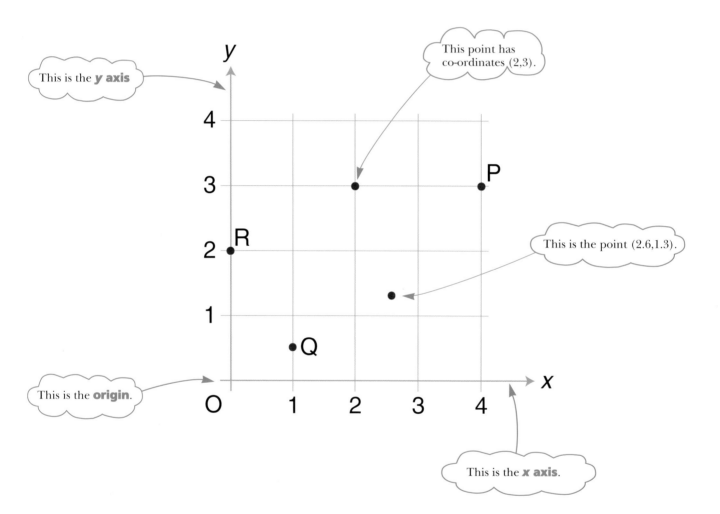

This is the **y axis**

This point has co-ordinates (2,3).

This is the point (2.6,1.3).

This is the **origin**.

This is the **x axis**.

The distance along the *x* axis is called the **x co-ordinate**.

The distance along the *y* axis is called the **y co-ordinate**.

The *x* (or horizontal) co-ordinate always comes first.

What are the co-ordinates of the origin, O?
What are the co-ordinates of points P, Q and R?

1 These diagrams show the positions of the stars in two well-known constellations.
For each constellation, list the co-ordinates of all its stars.

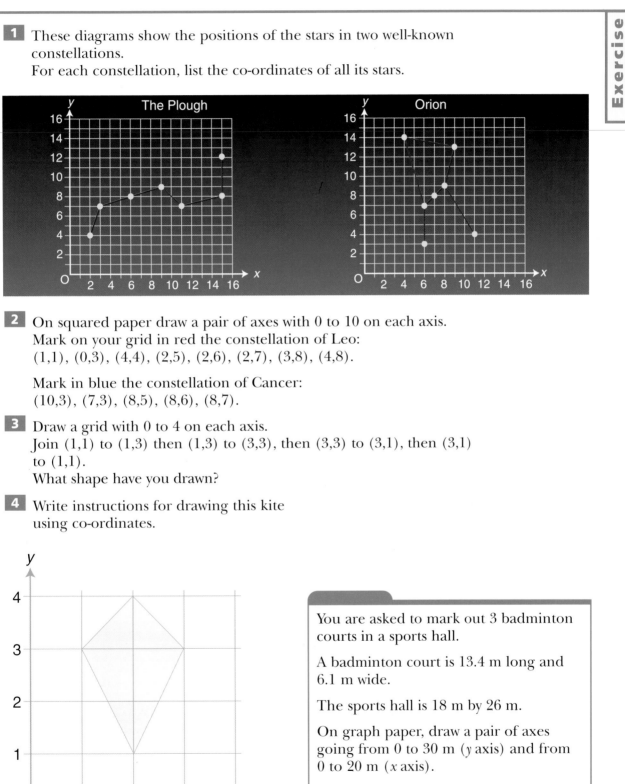

2 On squared paper draw a pair of axes with 0 to 10 on each axis.
Mark on your grid in red the constellation of Leo:
(1,1), (0,3), (4,4), (2,5), (2,6), (2,7), (3,8), (4,8).

Mark in blue the constellation of Cancer:
(10,3), (7,3), (8,5), (8,6), (8,7).

3 Draw a grid with 0 to 4 on each axis.
Join (1,1) to (1,3) then (1,3) to (3,3), then (3,3) to (3,1), then (3,1)
to (1,1).
What shape have you drawn?

4 Write instructions for drawing this kite
using co-ordinates.

You are asked to mark out 3 badminton courts in a sports hall.

A badminton court is 13.4 m long and 6.1 m wide.

The sports hall is 18 m by 26 m.

On graph paper, draw a pair of axes going from 0 to 30 m (*y* axis) and from 0 to 20 m (*x* axis).

Draw a plan of the hall with one corner at the origin. Give the co-ordinates of all the corners of each court.

Finishing off

> **Now that you have finished this chapter you should**
>
> ★ understand why grids are used on maps and diagrams
>
> ★ understand what is meant by x axis, y axis and origin
>
> ★ be able to write down the x and y co-ordinates of a point on a grid
>
> ★ be able to plot a point using its co-ordinates

Use the questions in the next exercise to check that you understand everything.

Mixed exercise

1

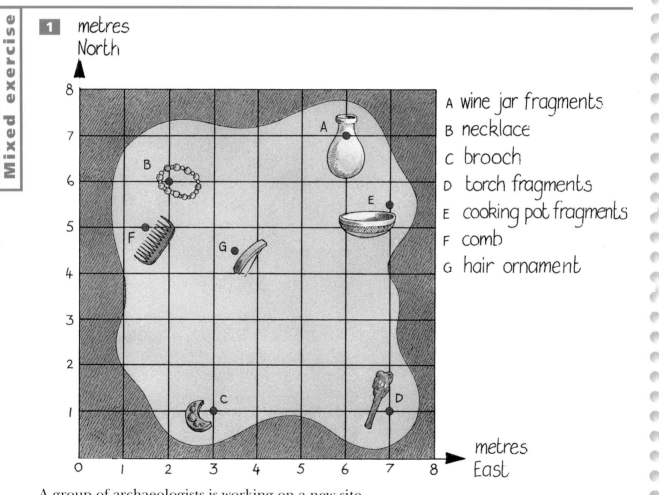

A wine jar fragments
B necklace
C brooch
D torch fragments
E cooking pot fragments
F comb
G hair ornament

A group of archaeologists is working on a new site.

There have been several finds already.

They have recorded the position of each find as a dot on this plan.

Write down the co-ordinates of each find.

2 On a piece of squared paper draw a 10 × 10 grid.
Join these points:
(2,2), (2,9), (3,9), (3,6), (6,6), (6,9), (7,9), (7,2), (6,2), (6,5),
(3,5), (3,2) and back to (2,2).
Shade in the shape you have made.
What letter of the alphabet is it?

3 Find a partner. You are going to play a game called battleships.

This version of the game uses co-ordinates.

You will both need a 10 × 10 grid, with *x* and *y* axes on it.

Draw on your grid one 'submarine', one 'frigate' and one 'battleship' (see diagram).

Choose your own positions, and don't let your partner see.

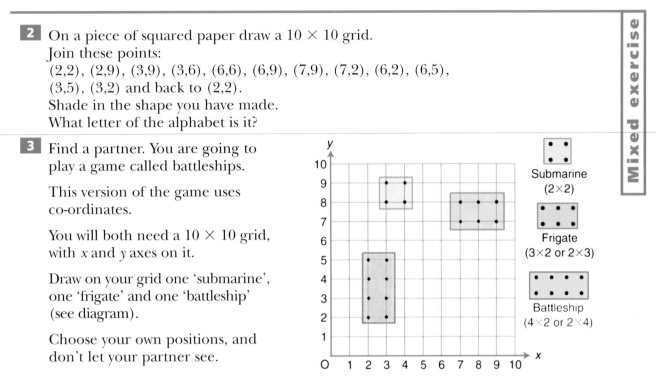

Submarine (2×2)

Frigate (3×2 or 2×3)

Battleship (4×2 or 2×4)

The rules

Take it in turns to choose a pair of whole number co-ordinates.

You score a 'hit' when you pick a point **inside** one of your opponent's ships.

When you score a 'hit' your partner must cross out that point, and say what type of ship you have hit.

You get an extra turn when you score a 'hit'.

A ship is sunk when all the points inside it have been 'hit'.

The winner is the one to sink all the opponent's ships.

This grid is used in calculator displays.

Each line can be lit up.

The diagram shows how the calculator displays the number 3.

Draw diagrams for as many other numbers and letters as you can.

Which letters and numbers can you not draw? Which are you unable to tell apart?

Two

Using numbers

Length

What is your handspan?

How far away is the nearest airport?

How thick is a pencil lead?

How tall are you?

What would you use to measure these lengths? Here are some ideas.

ruler

micrometer

trundle wheel

tape measure

069142

car mileometer

You can measure lengths in inches, feet, yards or miles.

These units are from the **Imperial system**.

> 12 Inches = 1 foot
> 3 feet = 1 yard
> 1760 yards = 1 mile

You can measure lengths in millimetres (mm), centimetres (cm), metres (m) or kilometres (km).

These units are from the **metric system**.

> 10 mm = 1 cm
> 100 cm = 1 m
> 1000 m = 1 km

You sometimes need to change lengths from Imperial to metric units (or the other way). When you just need a rough answer, you can use these conversions:

39 inches is about 1 m
1 foot is about 30 cm
$\frac{5}{8}$ mile is about 1 km.

When you need to estimate lengths, you will find it helpful to remember things like

the end of my thumb is about 1 inch long
the span of my hand is about 20 cm
1 pace is about 1 m.

Measure the widths of all your finger nails.
Which one is closest to 1 cm?

Measure the distance from your nose to the end of your outstretched arm.
How near is this to 1 m?

Using numbers

1 How many centimetres are there in   a) 2 m?   b) 4 m?

2 How many metres are there in   a) 5 km?   b) 8 km?

3 How many millimetres are there in   a) 3 cm?   b) 9 cm?

4 How many centimetres are there in   a) 20 mm?   b) 35 mm?

5 Greg drives from Bristol to Brighton. Here is a map of his journey.

a) How far has he driven when he gets to Southampton?

b) How far has he driven when he gets to Brighton?

c) Which is the longest part of the journey?

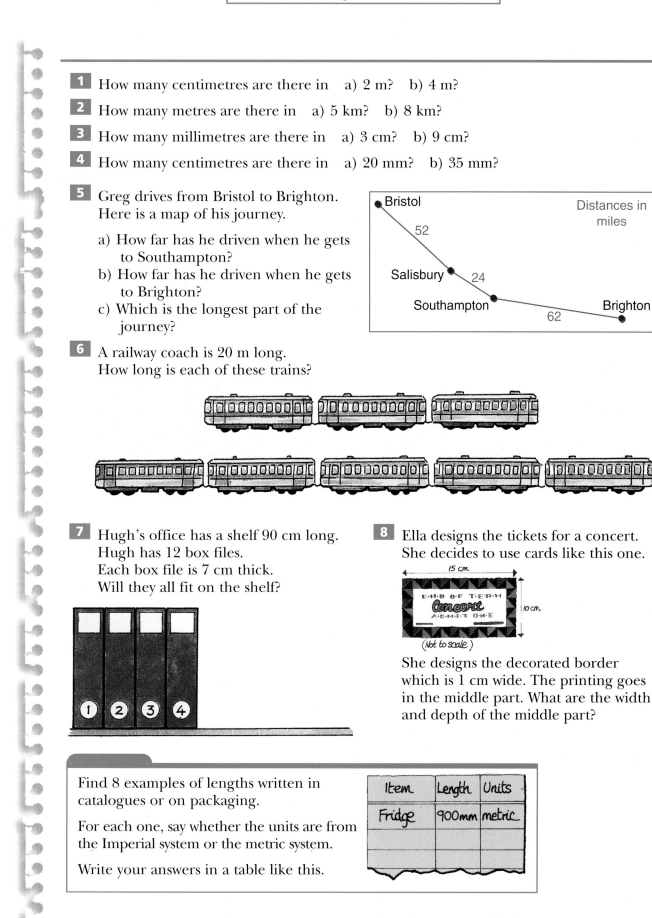

Bristol
Distances in miles
52
Salisbury   24
Southampton   Brighton
62

6 A railway coach is 20 m long.
How long is each of these trains?

7 Hugh's office has a shelf 90 cm long.
Hugh has 12 box files.
Each box file is 7 cm thick.
Will they all fit on the shelf?

8 Ella designs the tickets for a concert.
She decides to use cards like this one.

15 cm

E·N·D O·F T·E·R·M
Concert
A·D·M·I·T O·N·E

10 cm

(Not to scale)

She designs the decorated border which is 1 cm wide. The printing goes in the middle part. What are the width and depth of the middle part?

Find 8 examples of lengths written in catalogues or on packaging.

For each one, say whether the units are from the Imperial system or the metric system.

Write your answers in a table like this.

Item	Length	Units
Fridge	900mm	metric

13

Weight and mass

This cat is 3 kilograms, or just over $6\frac{1}{2}$ pounds.

In everyday English this is called the cat's **weight**.
In Science the word **mass** is used instead.

 What is the mass of a leaf?

What is the mass of a person?

What is the mass of a car?

How would you measure these?

You can measure masses in ounces (oz),
pounds (lb), stones or tons.
These units are from the Imperial system.

```
16 oz = 1 lb
14 lb = 1 stone
160 stone = 1 ton
```

You can measure masses in grams (g),
kilograms (kg) or tonnes.
These units are from the metric system.

```
1000 g = 1 kg
1000 kg = 1 tonne
```

You sometimes need to change masses from Imperial to
metric units (or the other way). When you just need a rough answer
you can use these conversions:

    1 oz is about 28 g
    2.2 lb is about 1 kg
    1 ton is about 1 tonne.

 An airline gives a baggage allowance of 30 kg.
How many pounds is this?

Capacity

This petrol can holds 5 litres, or just over 1 gallon.
This is the **capacity** of the can.

 What is the capacity of a teacup?

What is the capacity of a bucket?

You can measure capacity in pints or gallons.
These units are from the Imperial system.

```
8 pints = 1 gallon
```

You can measure capacity in millilitres (ml) or litres (l).
These units are from the metric system.

```
1000 ml = 1 L
```

When you need to convert from Imperial to metric units
(or the other way), these rough conversions are helpful:

    $1\frac{3}{4}$ pints is about 1 litre

    1 gallon is about $4\frac{1}{2}$ litres.

1 Write
   a) 1 kg in grams
   b) 500 g in kilograms
   c) 2 litres in millilitres
   d) $\frac{1}{2}$ gallon in pints.

2 Tony is shopping for his large family.
   a) He buys 4 bags of potatoes, each containing 5 kg.
      What is the total weight of the potatoes?

   b) He needs 1 kg of margarine. The biggest tubs in the shop
      contain 500 g each.
      How many of these tubs should Tony buy?

   c) Tony buys 2 kg of rice. How many grams is this?

   d) He buys 5 kg of onions. How many grams is this?

3 Guy weighs 8 stone 10 pounds. How many pounds is this?

4 Tom (105 kg), Fay (65 kg), Jenny (55 kg),
Richard (80 kg) and Jill (70 kg) get into
a lift. They see this notice in the lift.

   a) Can they all ride together in the lift safely?

   b) Jill offers to use the stairs. Can the other 4
      go together in the lift?

   c) Richard offers to use the stairs instead. Can the other 4 go
      together in the lift?

Max. Load
300 kg

5 Mandy's baby needs 200 ml of milk at
each feed.
How many feeds can Mandy get out of

   a) a 1-litre carton of ready-to-drink
      baby milk?

   b) a tin of baby milk powder that
      makes 5 litres?

6 Helga's doctor has given her a bottle
of medicine containing 140 ml. She is
to take a 5 ml dose 4 times a day.

   a) How many 5 ml doses are in the
      bottle?

   b) How many days will the bottle last?

Find 8 examples of weights (or masses)
written in catalogues or on packaging.

Find 8 examples of capacity.

For each one, say whether the units are
from the metric system or the Imperial
system. Make a table like this.

Item	Weight or Capacity	Units
Coffee	200g	Metric

Time

How long does it take to run a mile?
How long does it take to boil an egg?

How would you measure these times?

> 60 seconds = 1 minute
>
> 60 minutes = 1 hour

Jesse Owens ran 100 m in 10.2 seconds in 1936.

Clock times

There are 24 hours in a day.

This clock shows only 12 hours. You have to decide whether it is before noon (am) or after noon (pm) when you read the time from it.

This digital clock shows times from 00:00 to 23:59. It is a **24-hour clock**.

Current time

This central heating timer shows both systems. You can see how to convert 24-hour clock times to 12-hour clock times.

Timetables

Hertford Bus Station	0820	0845	0920	0945
Ware Railway Station	0830	0855	0930	0955
Hundred Acre Estate	——	0905	——	1005
Hoddesdon	0840	0915	0940	1015
Broxbourne	0848	0923	0948	1023
Cheshunt Railway Sta.	0912	0947	1012	1047

These buses don't stop at Hundred Acre Estate.

Most timetables use the 24-hour clock, like this one.

Tina lives on Hundred Acre Estate.
She wants to go by bus to Broxbourne in time for a job interview at 10.15 am.

Which bus should Tina catch?

1 a) Change 120 minutes into hours.

   b) Change 90 seconds into minutes and seconds.

2 a) Change 3 minutes into seconds.

   b) Change 1 hour 15 minutes into minutes.

3 An athletics team has 4 runners who take 51 seconds, 52 seconds, 53 seconds and 49 seconds for the legs of a 4 × 400 metre relay. How long, in minutes and seconds, do they take altogether?

4 Write these times using the 24-hour clock.

   a) 4.35 am   b) 5.40 pm   c) 9.20 pm   d) 1.50 pm

5 Write these 24-hour clock times using am or pm.

   a) 0825   b) 1430   c) 2345   d) 1815

6 a) For how many hours in the week is this shop open?

   b) Is it open at 4 pm on Saturday?

   c) Is it open at 7 pm on Monday?

7 a) How long does the News last?

   b) How long does the Local news last?

   c) What programme is on at quarter to seven?

   d) How long does Tennis highlights last?

8 Use the bus timetable opposite for this question.

   a) Lindsey wants to be at Ware Railway Station by 9 am. What is the latest bus that she can catch from Hertford?

   b) Liam lives in Hoddesdon and wants to be at Cheshunt Railway Station by 1010. What is the latest bus that he can catch?

Find a real timetable.

Rewrite the timetable (or part of it), changing the times to 24-hour clock times (or vice versa).

Why is the 24-hour clock useful?

Money

Example

Denise is a businesswoman. She books in at a hotel on Monday at £50 per night and she leaves on Friday morning.

a)   How many nights does she stay at the hotel?

b)   How much does it cost?

Solution

a)   Mon   Tue   Wed   Thur   Fri

1   2   3   4

> Notice that there are 5 days but only 4 nights.

b)   The cost of the stay is 4 × £50 = £200.

Booking a holiday

This chart shows the price (in pounds) of a holiday in Minorca in July for one person sharing a twin room.

Hotel	Blue Water		Golden Sand	
Room	Twin		Twin	
Board	Half Board		Full Board	
Departure	7 Nights	14 Nights	7 Nights	14 Nights
6Jul-12Jul	415	639	465	729
13Jul-19Jul	449	669	505	759
20Jul-9Aug	489	729	525	789
Supplements per person per night	Single room £3		Single room £4	
	Sea view £3		Balcony £5	
	Full board £10			

Andrew and Verity want 14 nights at Hotel Blue Water, starting on 8 July. They want a twin room with a sea view.

The travel agent works out the cost.

```
14 nights, Hotel Blue Water
         dep. July 8th:      £    639   each
Sea view: 14 nights X £3:    £     42   each
                             £    681   each
              2 people:            x 2
                             £   1362   total
                             (plus insurance)
```

 How much money do they save if they decide not to have a room with a sea view?

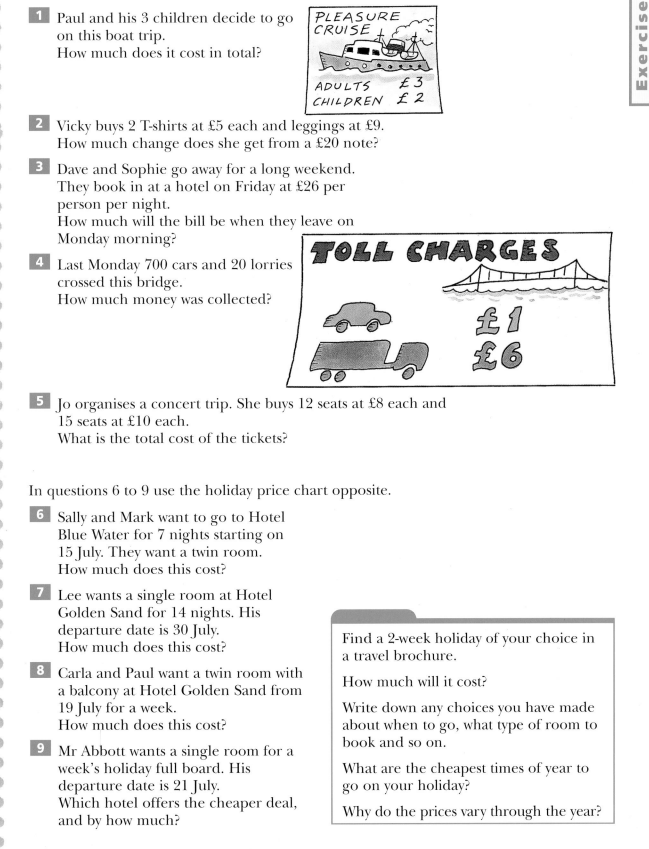

1 Paul and his 3 children decide to go on this boat trip. How much does it cost in total?

PLEASURE CRUISE

ADULTS £3
CHILDREN £2

2 Vicky buys 2 T-shirts at £5 each and leggings at £9. How much change does she get from a £20 note?

3 Dave and Sophie go away for a long weekend. They book in at a hotel on Friday at £26 per person per night. How much will the bill be when they leave on Monday morning?

4 Last Monday 700 cars and 20 lorries crossed this bridge. How much money was collected?

TOLL CHARGES

£1
£6

5 Jo organises a concert trip. She buys 12 seats at £8 each and 15 seats at £10 each. What is the total cost of the tickets?

In questions 6 to 9 use the holiday price chart opposite.

6 Sally and Mark want to go to Hotel Blue Water for 7 nights starting on 15 July. They want a twin room. How much does this cost?

7 Lee wants a single room at Hotel Golden Sand for 14 nights. His departure date is 30 July. How much does this cost?

8 Carla and Paul want a twin room with a balcony at Hotel Golden Sand from 19 July for a week. How much does this cost?

9 Mr Abbott wants a single room for a week's holiday full board. His departure date is 21 July. Which hotel offers the cheaper deal, and by how much?

Find a 2-week holiday of your choice in a travel brochure.

How much will it cost?

Write down any choices you have made about when to go, what type of room to book and so on.

What are the cheapest times of year to go on your holiday?

Why do the prices vary through the year?

Finishing off

> **Now that you have finished this chapter you should be able to**
>
> ★ find length, mass, capacity and time
>
> ★ change a quantity from one unit to another
>
> ★ use the 24-hour clock and timetables
>
> ★ do money calculations

Use the questions in the next exercise to check that you understand everything.

Mixed exercise

1 a) How many millimetres are there in 4 cm?

b) How many grams are there in 4 kg?

c) How many litres is 3000 ml?

d) How many seconds are there in 5 minutes?

2 Kelly weighed 49 kg last year. She now weighs 52 kg. How much weight has she gained?

3 Louise is stocking the chill-cabinets of a supermarket. She has a trolley with 4 shelves. There are 12 containers on each shelf. Each container holds 6 pints of milk.

a) How many containers are there on the trolley?

b) How many pints of milk are there on the trolley?

4 Greg's Monday morning timetable is shown here.

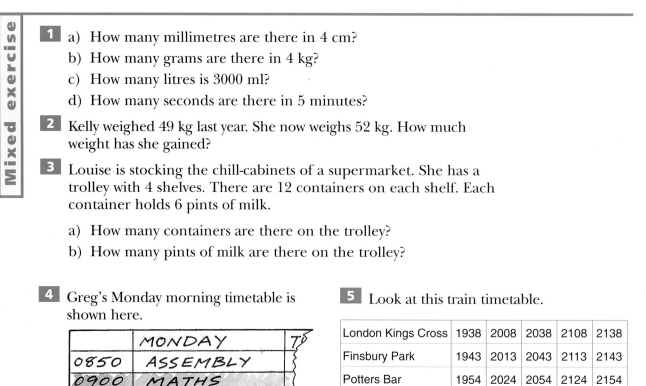

	MONDAY	T
0850	ASSEMBLY	
0900	MATHS	
0940	SCIENCE	
1020	BREAK	
1035	FRENCH	
1115	TECHNOLOGY	
1155	LUNCH	

a) For how long, in hours and minutes, is he in lessons?

b) How long, in hours and minutes, does the morning last?

5 Look at this train timetable.

London Kings Cross	1938	2008	2038	2108	2138
Finsbury Park	1943	2013	2043	2113	2143
Potters Bar	1954	2024	2054	2124	2154
Hatfield	2000	2030	2100	2130	2200
Welwyn Garden City	2004	2034	2104	2134	2204

a) How long does the 2038 train take to travel from Kings Cross to Welwyn Garden City?

b) Carys gets to Kings Cross at 9.30 pm. She catches the next train to Potters Bar. What time does she arrive?

6 Charlotte arrives at this guest house on Sunday evening and books to stay until Friday morning. She is too late for an evening meal on Sunday but orders it for the other nights.

How much is her bill?

Bed and Breakfast £18
Evening Meal £7

7 This table shows the price (in pounds) of a holiday in Crete for one person sharing a twin room.

Apartment	**Cliffedge**		**Beachside**	
Departure date	*7 Nights*	*14 Nights*	*7 Nights*	*14 Nights*
21Jul-11Aug	399	475	429	499
12Aug-19Aug	395	469	425	495
20Aug-28Aug	375	445	399	475
Supplements (per person per night)	Single room £4		Single room £3	
	Sea view £3		Sea view £2	

a) Andrea and Tim want to start their 7-night holiday on 13 August. They would like to book 7 nights at Beachside with a sea view.

How much does this cost?

b) Jodie wants a single at Cliffedge for 14 nights, departing on 3 August.

How much does this cost?

This chart from a road atlas shows the distances in miles between 6 cities.

a) You can see that the distance from Southampton to Newcastle is 323 miles, but you need to travel from Southampton to Newcastle passing through all the other cities on the way.

Cambridge is 61 miles from London

Birmingham					
101	Cambridge				
108	207	Cardiff			
120	61	155	London		
202	230	318	285	Newcastle	
129	132	141	80	323	Southampton

Look at a map and decide which orders are sensible.

Find the one with the shortest total distance.

b) Make your own distance chart for 6 towns or villages near you.

Three

Types of number

Types of number

Debbie works for a food and drink company.

She decides how items are packaged together so that customers can buy in bulk.

Multiples

Debbie decides that tins of tea should be packaged in pairs.

 How many tins are there in 4 packages?

How many tins are there in 5 packages?

1 package   2 packages   3 packages

The numbers of tins,   2, 4, 6, 8, 10, …   are called the **multiples** of 2.

They are the answers to
the 2× table: $1 \times 2 = 2$
$2 \times 2 = 4$
$3 \times 2 = 6$
and so on.

> The multiples of 2 are the **even** numbers.
> The other numbers,
> 1, 3, 5, 7, …, are **odd**.

Factors

Debbie thinks that small bottles of Supa Juice will sell well in packages of 12.

Debbie designs this package.

It has 3 rows of 4.

Supa Juice
12 Bottles

$3 \times 4 = 12$. We say that 3 and 4 are **factors** of 12.

There are other ways of arranging 12 bottles in a rectangular package.

 Draw 2 other ways of arranging 12 bottles in a rectangular package.

The different arrangements tell you all the factors of 12.

You may have thought of 6 rows of 2. $6 \times 2 = 12$.

You may have thought of 1 row of 12. $1 \times 12 = 12$.

> It is often useful to list the factors in order, like this.

The factors of 12 are   1, 2, 3, 4, 6 and 12.

Another way of saying this is that 12 is **divisible** by 1, 2, 3, 4, 6 and 12.

Types of number

1 Prem is delivering post to houses in Aspen Road.

He has post for numbers 8, 13, 21, 36, 44 and 47.

a) Write down the odd numbers.
b) Write down the even numbers.
c) How do you know which numbers are odd and which are even?
d) Prem delivers to the houses in order. How many times does he cross the road?

2 Here is a box of chocolate eclairs.

How many eclairs are there in

a) 2 boxes?   b) 3 boxes?   c) 4 boxes?

3 Sue is catering for a party.

She needs 50 eggs.

How many boxes does she need to buy?

4 Lucy has 18 cork tiles.

She wants to use them to make a rectangular noticeboard in her room.

She sketches this arrangement.

a) Draw all the other ways of making a rectangular noticeboard using exactly 18 tiles.
b) Now list all the factors of 18.

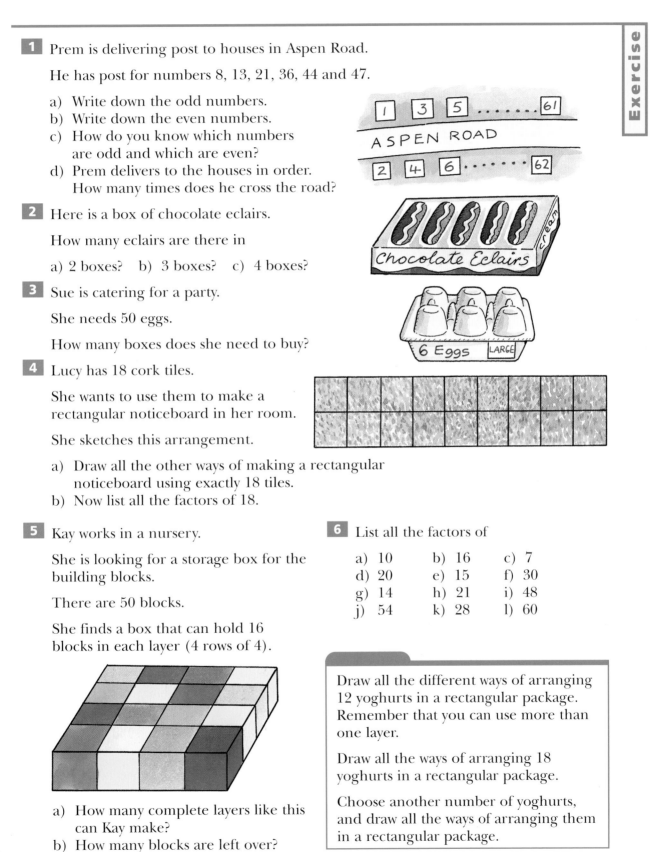

5 Kay works in a nursery.

She is looking for a storage box for the building blocks.

There are 50 blocks.

She finds a box that can hold 16 blocks in each layer (4 rows of 4).

a) How many complete layers like this can Kay make?
b) How many blocks are left over?

6 List all the factors of

a) 10   b) 16   c) 7
d) 20   e) 15   f) 30
g) 14   h) 21   i) 48
j) 54   k) 28   l) 60

Draw all the different ways of arranging 12 yoghurts in a rectangular package. Remember that you can use more than one layer.

Draw all the ways of arranging 18 yoghurts in a rectangular package.

Choose another number of yoghurts, and draw all the ways of arranging them in a rectangular package.

Prime numbers

Lauren goes on holiday to Portugal.

She likes the traditional tiles that she sees.

She wants to make 2 rows of 4 tiles above her hand basin at home, so she buys 8 identical square tiles.

Sadly, one tile gets broken on the way home. Only 7 are left.

How can Lauren arrange these in a rectangle?

There are only two ways.

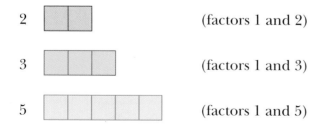

The different rectangles you can make tell you the factors of a number. 7 has only two factors, 1 and 7.

7 is an example of a **prime number**

A prime number has just two different factors, 1 and itself.

 How can you tell that 8 is not a prime number?

The first three prime numbers are

2   (factors 1 and 2)

3   (factors 1 and 3)

5   (factors 1 and 5)

 What is the next prime number?

What are the next four after that?

Can you find a quick way of identifying prime numbers?

1 Work out whether each of these is a prime number.

a) 24   b) 23   c) 75   d) 31
e) 39   f) 82   g) 101   h) 236

Investigation

1 **Finding prime numbers**

Eratosthenes lived from 276 – 194 BC (approximately).

One of the things for which he is famous is this method of finding prime numbers. It is called the 'Sieve of Eratosthenes'.

Get (or draw) a 10 × 10 number square like this, and follow these steps.

- Cross out 1

- Leave 2, but cross out all other multiples of 2 (4, 6, 8, ..., 100)

- Leave 3, but cross out all other multiples of 3 (6, 9, 12, ..., 99)

- 4 has already been crossed out so move on to 5

- Leave 5, but cross out all other multiples of 5 (10, 15, 20, ...)

- Continue in this way for 6, 7, 8, 9 and 10.

1	2	3	4	5	6	7	8	9	10
11	12	13	14	15	16	17	18	19	20
21	22	23	24	25	26	27	28	29	30
31	32	33	34	35	36	37	38	39	40
41	42	43	44	45	46	47	48	49	50
51	52	53	54	55	56	57	58	59	60
61	62	63	64	65	66	67	68	69	70
71	72	73	74	75	76	77	78	79	80
81	82	83	84	85	86	87	88	89	90
91	92	93	94	95	96	97	98	99	100

How many numbers are left uncrossed?
These are all the prime numbers less than 100.

You stopped following the steps at 10.
Why didn't you have to follow the steps all the way up to 100? (You might like to discuss this with your group. The reason isn't easy to see.)

You are writing a quiz to raise money for your youth group.
You decide to do a 'fill in the blanks' game about numbers.
Here is the first question.

11 p_____ in a f_____ t_____

The correct answer is

11 p<u>layers</u>   in a f<u>ootball</u>   t<u>eam</u>

Make up 10 questions like this, using only prime numbers. (You can use the same number in more than one question.)

Squares, square roots and cubes

Ramesh designs products for a chocolate manufacturer.

He has designed a range of chocolate squares.

Here are the first three sizes:

$1 \times 1 = 1$ $2 \times 2 = 4$ $3 \times 3 = 9$

 How many pieces would there be in a 4×4 square?

How many in a 5×5 square?

The numbers 1, 4, 9, 16, 25, … are called **squares**, or **square numbers**.

A quick way of writing 4×4 is 4^2.

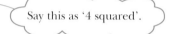

Similarly, 5×5 is 5^2, and so on.

Say this as '4 squared'.

Ramesh's largest chocolate square has 36 pieces.

You know that

$6^2 = 6 \times 6 = 36$

A square with 36 pieces must have 6 pieces along each side.

You can write $\sqrt{36} = 6$.

The **square root** of 36 is 6.

Similarly, a square with 25 pieces has 5 pieces along each side.
You can write $\sqrt{25} = 5$.

Ramesh is working on a 'chocolate cube' for the Christmas market.

Each cube is made up of smaller cubes.

Here are the first three sizes:

 How many chocolate cubes are there in the $3 \times 3 \times 3$ cube?

The numbers 1, 8, 27, … are called **cubes**, or **cube numbers**.

A quick way of writing $2 \times 2 \times 2$ is 2^3.

Say this as '2 cubed' or '2 to the power 3'.

1 Work out a) 5^2 b) 8^2 c) 9^2 d) 12^2 e) 20^2

2 Find the square root of

a) 25   b) 49   c) 100   d) 121   e) 400

(You will have to guess the square root, then check by squaring it.)

3 A chessboard is a large square divided into 64 smaller squares.

How many squares has it along each side?

4 During an earthquake appeal, Siba asks her friends to knit small squares. She collects the squares and sews them together to make square blankets.

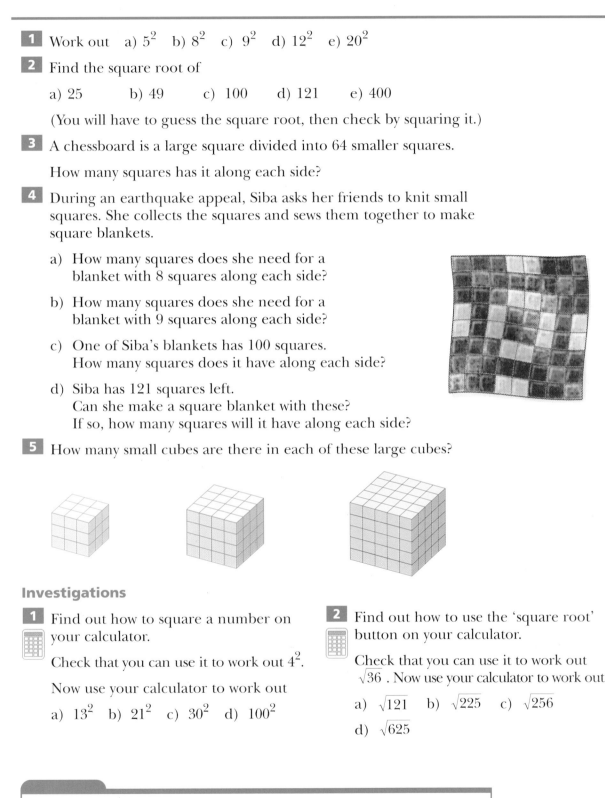

a) How many squares does she need for a blanket with 8 squares along each side?

b) How many squares does she need for a blanket with 9 squares along each side?

c) One of Siba's blankets has 100 squares. How many squares does it have along each side?

d) Siba has 121 squares left. Can she make a square blanket with these? If so, how many squares will it have along each side?

5 How many small cubes are there in each of these large cubes?

Investigations

1 Find out how to square a number on your calculator.

Check that you can use it to work out 4^2.

Now use your calculator to work out

a) 13^2 b) 21^2 c) 30^2 d) 100^2

2 Find out how to use the 'square root' button on your calculator.

Check that you can use it to work out $\sqrt{36}$. Now use your calculator to work out

a) $\sqrt{121}$ b) $\sqrt{225}$ c) $\sqrt{256}$

d) $\sqrt{625}$

Make a list of 6 everyday objects that are squares or cubes.

For each one, state as accurately as you can the length of one side.

Finishing off

Now that you have finished this chapter you should be able to

* ★ recognise odd and even numbers
* ★ find factors
* ★ work out multiples

* ★ recognise prime numbers
* ★ work out square numbers and cube numbers
* ★ find square roots

Use the questions in the next exercise to check that you understand everything.

Mixed exercise

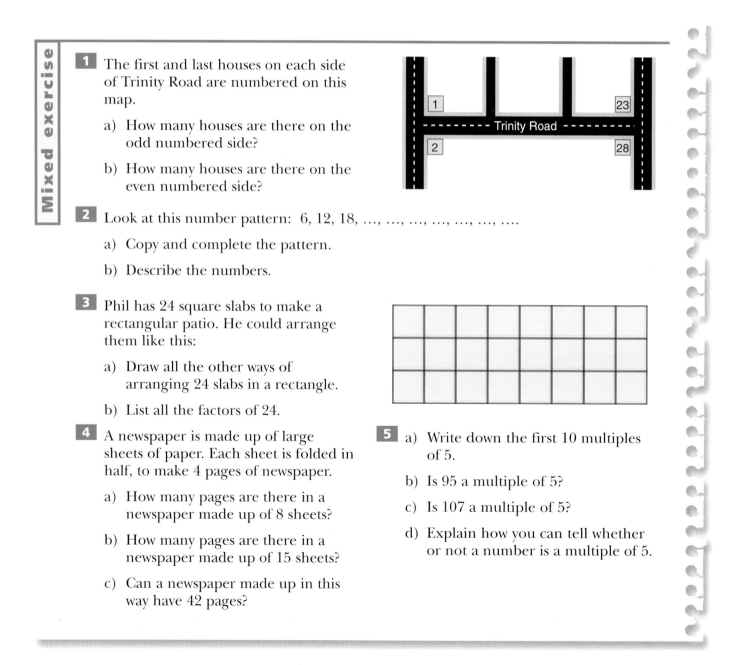

1 The first and last houses on each side of Trinity Road are numbered on this map.

  a) How many houses are there on the odd numbered side?

  b) How many houses are there on the even numbered side?

2 Look at this number pattern: 6, 12, 18, ..., ..., ..., ..., ..., ..., ...

  a) Copy and complete the pattern.

  b) Describe the numbers.

3 Phil has 24 square slabs to make a rectangular patio. He could arrange them like this:

  a) Draw all the other ways of arranging 24 slabs in a rectangle.

  b) List all the factors of 24.

4 A newspaper is made up of large sheets of paper. Each sheet is folded in half, to make 4 pages of newspaper.

  a) How many pages are there in a newspaper made up of 8 sheets?

  b) How many pages are there in a newspaper made up of 15 sheets?

  c) Can a newspaper made up in this way have 42 pages?

5 a) Write down the first 10 multiples of 5.

  b) Is 95 a multiple of 5?

  c) Is 107 a multiple of 5?

  d) Explain how you can tell whether or not a number is a multiple of 5.

6 List all the factors of   a) 8   b) 35   c) 42   d) 100

7 Which number in the following list is a prime?

  18   95   70   41   99

8 How many squares are needed for each of these patchwork designs?

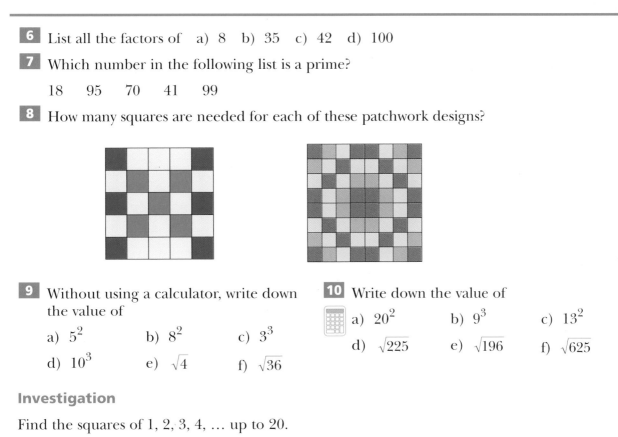

9 Without using a calculator, write down the value of

a) 5^2 b) 8^2 c) 3^3

d) 10^3 e) $\sqrt{4}$ f) $\sqrt{36}$

10 Write down the value of

a) 20^2 b) 9^3 c) 13^2

d) $\sqrt{225}$ e) $\sqrt{196}$ f) $\sqrt{625}$

Investigation

Find the squares of 1, 2, 3, 4, ... up to 20.

Write them in a table like this, so that you can look at the last digits of the square numbers. (A few have been done for you.)

Number	Square of number	Last digit of square
1	1	1
2	4	4
⋮		
8	64	4

Look at the numbers in the right hand column.

Do you think that a square number could end with the digit 2?

Could 213 643 be a square number?

Buy yourself a chocolate orange.

How many people can share it equally with none left over? (There are several answers.)

You eat one piece while no-one is looking. How many people can share it equally now?

29

Four

Symmetry

Reflection symmetry

Look at this picture of the Canadian flag.

If you stand a mirror on the dotted line, the flag will look exactly the same in the mirror as it does without the mirror.

The dotted line is a mirror line. It is also called a **line of reflection symmetry**.

The flag is symmetrical about this line.

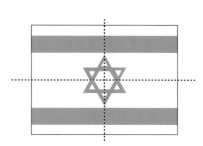

The Israeli flag has 2 lines of reflection symmetry. They are shown as dotted lines in the picture.

 Check that the flag looks the same when you stand a mirror on each dotted line.

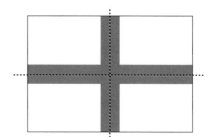

The English flag (the St George's Cross) also has 2 lines of reflection symmetry.

Do you think its diagonals are lines of reflection symmetry? Stand a mirror on the diagonal to find out.

The Swiss flag has 4 lines of reflection symmetry. One is vertical, one is horizontal, and the other 2 are diagonal. The lines of symmetry are shown on the diagram.

Check them using a mirror.

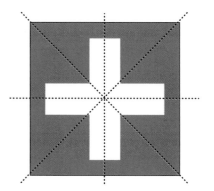

1 Which of these signs have reflection symmetry?

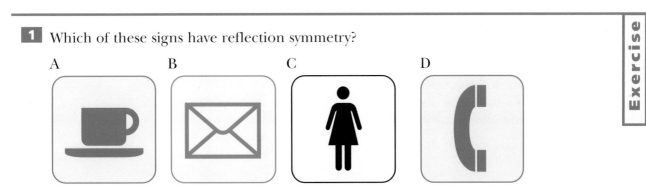

A   B   C   D

2 Write down how many lines of symmetry each of these shapes has.

Copy each diagram and draw on the lines of symmetry.

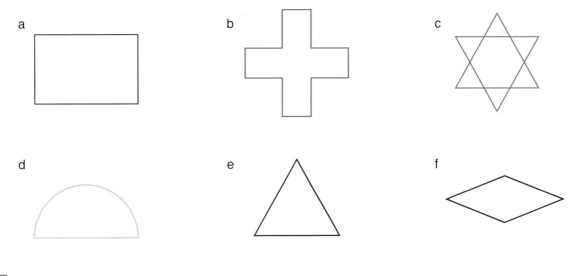

a

b

c

d

e

f

3 Make 3 copies of this diagram.

   a) On the first copy, shade 8 of the squares to make a pattern with 1 line of symmetry.

   b) On the second copy, shade 8 of the squares to make a pattern with 2 lines of symmetry.

   c) On the third copy, shade 8 of the squares to make a pattern with 4 lines of symmetry.

Design a symmetrical pattern for a tile for a bathroom wall.

Show how the tiles would fit together to make an overall pattern.

Drawing reflections

Sally is making a Christmas card. She is drawing a Christmas tree.

She wants both sides of the tree to be exactly the same, so that it has a line of reflection symmetry.

Sally has already drawn the left hand side of the tree.

How can she draw the other side so that it is exactly the same?

One way is to use tracing paper.

Sally traces her drawing and then turns the tracing over.

She uses the turned over tracing to draw the other half of the tree.

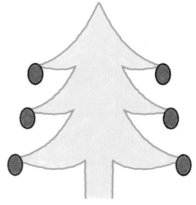

Another way to draw symmetrical shapes is to use squared paper or square dotted paper. You do not need to use tracing paper to draw the reflection. Instead, you use the squares (or dots) to help you, like this:

If there are 2 lines of reflection symmetry as in the next picture, reflect the shape in one of the lines first, then reflect the shape and its reflection in the other line.

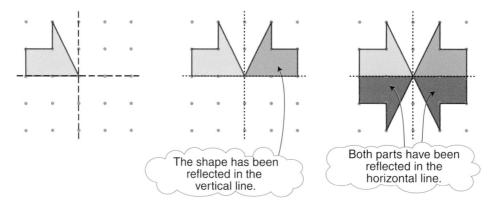

The shape has been reflected in the vertical line.

Both parts have been reflected in the horizontal line.

1 The dotted lines in the patterns below are lines of reflection symmetry. Copy the patterns on squared paper and draw the rest of each pattern.

2 Copy each of these patterns on square dotted paper, and draw the rest of it. (Again the dotted lines show the lines of reflection symmetry.)

3 Copy each of these shapes on square dotted paper. Draw its reflection in the line of symmetry shown.

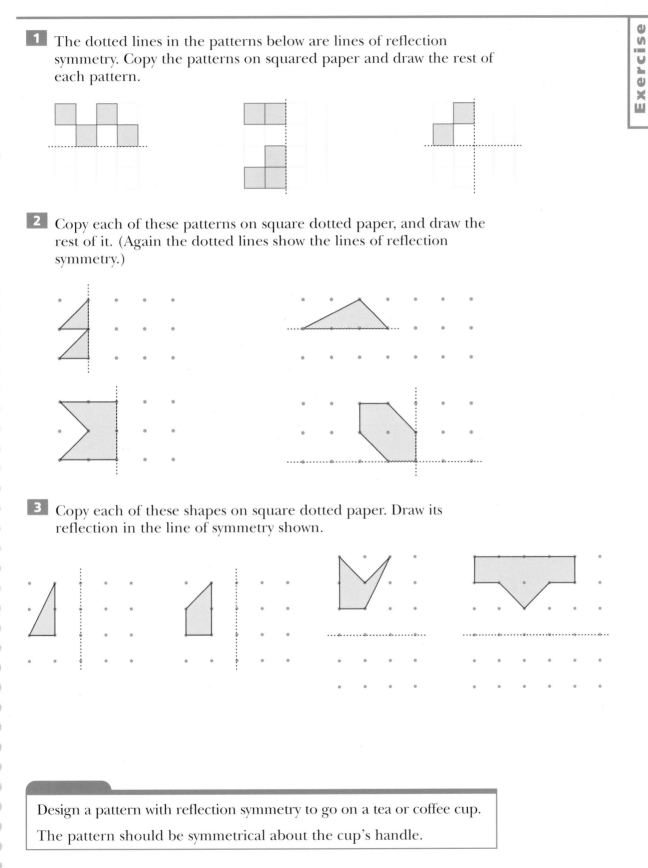

Design a pattern with reflection symmetry to go on a tea or coffee cup.

The pattern should be symmetrical about the cup's handle.

Rotational symmetry

The US dollar symbol has no lines of reflection symmetry. (You can check this using a mirror.)

However, it does have another kind of symmetry, called turn symmetry, or rotational symmetry.

 Trace the dollar symbol. Now turn your tracing round through half a turn, so that it is upside down. You should find that you can fit the tracing exactly over the dollar symbol.

The dollar symbol looks exactly the same in 2 different positions – the right way up and upside down.
It has **rotational symmetry with order 2**.

This is the symbol for recycling.

It can be turned so that it looks the same in 3 different positions. It has **rotational symmetry with order 3**.

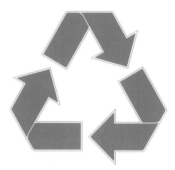

 Trace the symbol and check that the tracing will fit exactly over the symbol in 3 different positions.

Some patterns can have both reflection symmetry and rotational symmetry.

The symbol for First Aid has 4 lines of reflection symmetry. These are shown with dotted lines.

It looks the same if it is turned through a quarter turn, so it has
rotational symmetry with order 4

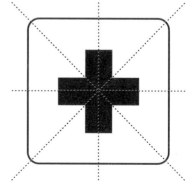

1 Which of these playing cards have rotational symmetry?

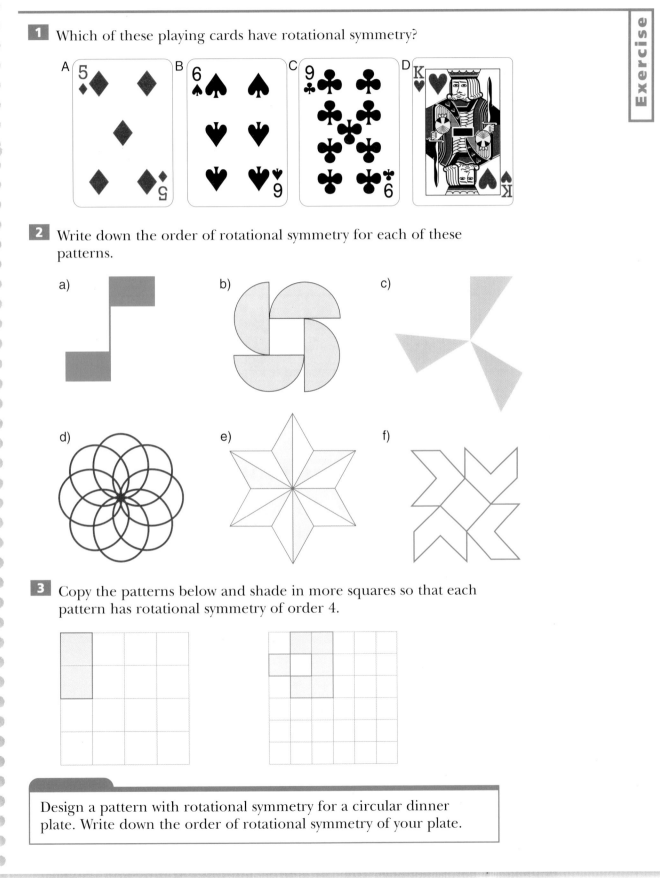

2 Write down the order of rotational symmetry for each of these patterns.

a)

b)

c)

d)

e)

f)

3 Copy the patterns below and shade in more squares so that each pattern has rotational symmetry of order 4.

Design a pattern with rotational symmetry for a circular dinner plate. Write down the order of rotational symmetry of your plate.

Finishing off

Now that you have finished this chapter you should be able to

★ say how many lines of reflection symmetry a shape or pattern has

★ complete a pattern so that it has 1 or 2 lines of symmetry

★ draw the reflection of a shape in a horizontal or vertical line

★ say whether a shape or pattern has rotational symmetry, and if it has, give the order of rotational symmetry

Use the questions in the next exercise to check that you understand everything.

1 For each of the logos below

a) say how many lines of reflection symmetry it has

b) say whether it has rotational symmetry, and if it has, what the order of rotational symmetry is.

i) Our Price   ii) NatWest   iii) McDonald's

iv) The Royal Bank of Scotland   v) British Rail

2 Copy the patterns below.

Complete them so that the dotted lines are lines of symmetry.

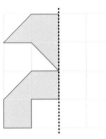 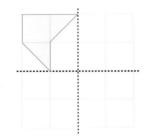

3 Copy the letters of the alphabet shown below on squared paper and reflect them in the lines shown.

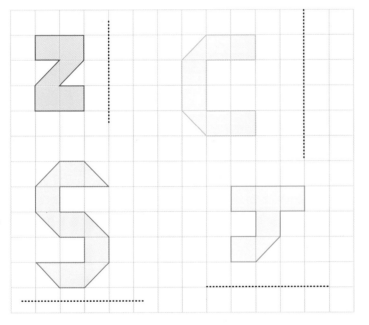

Investigation

a) How many patterns with just one line of symmetry can you make by shading squares in a 3 × 3 grid? (Shade complete squares only.)

b) How many patterns with 2 lines of symmetry can you make?

c) How many patterns with 4 lines of symmetry can you make?

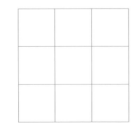

Using a 4 × 4 square grid, design a company logo and state what kinds of symmetry it has.

Example

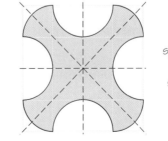

4 lines of symmetry and rotational symmetry of order 4.

Five

Fractions

Equivalent fractions

Alf and Mo have allotments of the same size.

Alf divides his allotment into 4 equal parts.

He plants potatoes in 1 of the 4 parts.

You can write 1 out of 4 as $\frac{1}{4}$.

We call it one quarter. $\frac{1}{4}$ is a **fraction**.

The top, sometimes called the **numerator**, is 1.

The bottom, sometimes called the **denominator**, is 4.

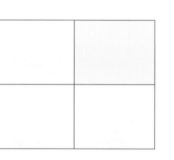

Mo divides her allotment into 8 equal parts.

She plants potatoes in 2 of the 8 parts.

You can write 2 out of 8 as $\frac{2}{8}$ (two eighths).

Look at the pictures of the allotments.

Who has the larger potato patch?

You can see that the patches are the same size.

$\frac{2}{8}$ is the same as $\frac{1}{4}$.

Elsa has an allotment too.

She has divided it up into 12 equal parts.

Elsa's potato patch is the same size as Alf's.
You can see that $\frac{3}{12}$, $\frac{2}{8}$ and $\frac{1}{4}$ all mean the
same thing.

They are **equivalent fractions**. They can
all be written as $\frac{1}{4}$.

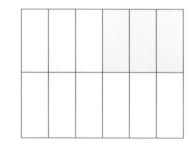

$\frac{1}{4}$ is the **simplest form** because it has the smallest numbers.

To find an equivalent fraction, you multiply (or divide) the top and
bottom by the same number

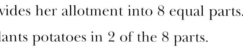

$$\frac{1}{3} \xrightarrow{\times 3} = \xrightarrow{\times 3} \frac{3}{9} \qquad \frac{2}{10} \xrightarrow{\div 2} = \xrightarrow{\div 2} \frac{1}{5}$$

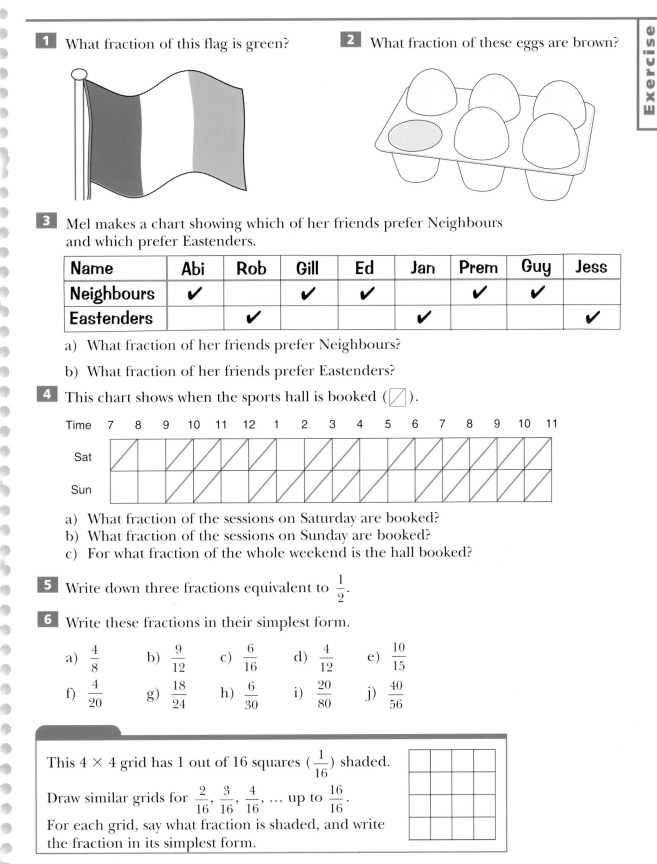

1 What fraction of this flag is green?

2 What fraction of these eggs are brown?

3 Mel makes a chart showing which of her friends prefer Neighbours and which prefer Eastenders.

Name	Abi	Rob	Gill	Ed	Jan	Prem	Guy	Jess
Neighbours	✔		✔	✔		✔	✔	
Eastenders		✔			✔			✔

a) What fraction of her friends prefer Neighbours?

b) What fraction of her friends prefer Eastenders?

4 This chart shows when the sports hall is booked (▨).

Time 7 8 9 10 11 12 1 2 3 4 5 6 7 8 9 10 11

Sat

Sun

a) What fraction of the sessions on Saturday are booked?
b) What fraction of the sessions on Sunday are booked?
c) For what fraction of the whole weekend is the hall booked?

5 Write down three fractions equivalent to $\frac{1}{2}$.

6 Write these fractions in their simplest form.

a) $\frac{4}{8}$　　b) $\frac{9}{12}$　　c) $\frac{6}{16}$　　d) $\frac{4}{12}$　　e) $\frac{10}{15}$

f) $\frac{4}{20}$　　g) $\frac{18}{24}$　　h) $\frac{6}{30}$　　i) $\frac{20}{80}$　　j) $\frac{40}{56}$

This 4 × 4 grid has 1 out of 16 squares ($\frac{1}{16}$) shaded.

Draw similar grids for $\frac{2}{16}, \frac{3}{16}, \frac{4}{16}, \ldots$ up to $\frac{16}{16}$.

For each grid, say what fraction is shaded, and write the fraction in its simplest form.

Adding and subtracting fractions (1)

Martina and Gary have ordered a pizza. It has been cut into 8 equal parts.

Martina eats 3 of the 8 pieces. She eats $\frac{3}{8}$.

Gary eats 4 pieces. He eats $\frac{4}{8}$.

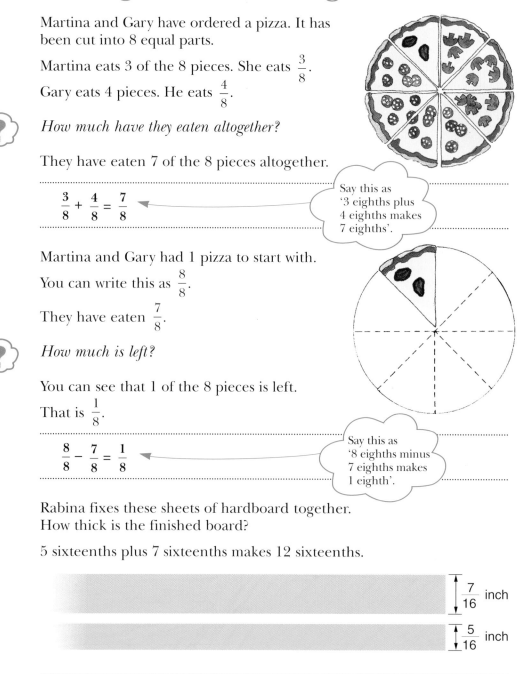

How much have they eaten altogether?

They have eaten 7 of the 8 pieces altogether.

$$\frac{3}{8} + \frac{4}{8} = \frac{7}{8}$$

Say this as '3 eighths plus 4 eighths makes 7 eighths'.

Martina and Gary had 1 pizza to start with.

You can write this as $\frac{8}{8}$.

They have eaten $\frac{7}{8}$.

How much is left?

You can see that 1 of the 8 pieces is left.

That is $\frac{1}{8}$.

$$\frac{8}{8} - \frac{7}{8} = \frac{1}{8}$$

Say this as '8 eighths minus 7 eighths makes 1 eighth'.

Rabina fixes these sheets of hardboard together.
How thick is the finished board?

5 sixteenths plus 7 sixteenths makes 12 sixteenths.

$\frac{7}{16}$ inch

$\frac{5}{16}$ inch

$$\frac{5}{16} + \frac{7}{16} = \frac{12}{16}$$

$\frac{12}{16}$ in its simplest form is $\frac{3}{4}$

The finished board will be $\frac{12}{16}$ inch thick.

Adding and subtracting fractions is easy when the denominators are the same.

Practise it by doing the questions opposite.

Fractions

1 Work these out. Give your answers in their simplest form.

a) $\dfrac{1}{4} + \dfrac{1}{4}$

b) $\dfrac{5}{8} + \dfrac{1}{8}$

c) $\dfrac{3}{8} - \dfrac{1}{8}$

d) $\dfrac{3}{16} + \dfrac{7}{16}$

e) $\dfrac{1}{2} + \dfrac{1}{2}$

f) $\dfrac{5}{16} - \dfrac{3}{16}$

g) $\dfrac{3}{4} + \dfrac{1}{4}$

h) $\dfrac{9}{16} - \dfrac{5}{16}$

2 Carl buys a chocolate bar. There are 8 pieces of chocolate in the bar. Carl eats 3 pieces and his brother eats 2 pieces.

a) What fraction of the bar do the boys eat?
b) What fraction of the bar is left?

3 In each of these, copy out the sum and fill in the missing number.

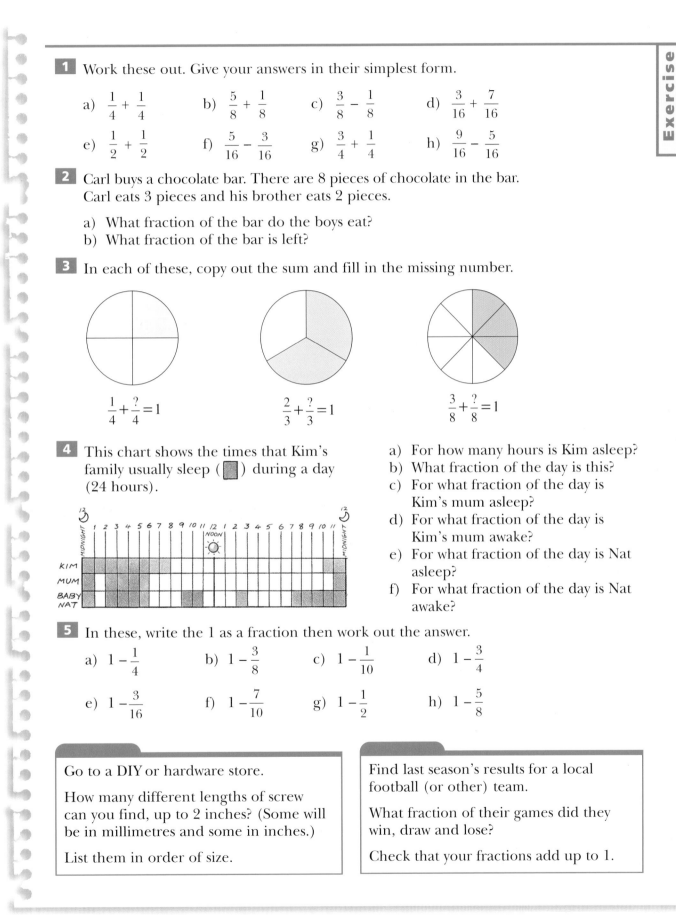

$\dfrac{1}{4} + \dfrac{?}{4} = 1$

$\dfrac{2}{3} + \dfrac{?}{3} = 1$

$\dfrac{3}{8} + \dfrac{?}{8} = 1$

4 This chart shows the times that Kim's family usually sleep (▨) during a day (24 hours).

a) For how many hours is Kim asleep?
b) What fraction of the day is this?
c) For what fraction of the day is Kim's mum asleep?
d) For what fraction of the day is Kim's mum awake?
e) For what fraction of the day is Nat asleep?
f) For what fraction of the day is Nat awake?

5 In these, write the 1 as a fraction then work out the answer.

a) $1 - \dfrac{1}{4}$

b) $1 - \dfrac{3}{8}$

c) $1 - \dfrac{1}{10}$

d) $1 - \dfrac{3}{4}$

e) $1 - \dfrac{3}{16}$

f) $1 - \dfrac{7}{10}$

g) $1 - \dfrac{1}{2}$

h) $1 - \dfrac{5}{8}$

Go to a DIY or hardware store.

How many different lengths of screw can you find, up to 2 inches? (Some will be in millimetres and some in inches.)

List them in order of size.

Find last season's results for a local football (or other) team.

What fraction of their games did they win, draw and lose?

Check that your fractions add up to 1.

Adding and subtracting fractions (2)

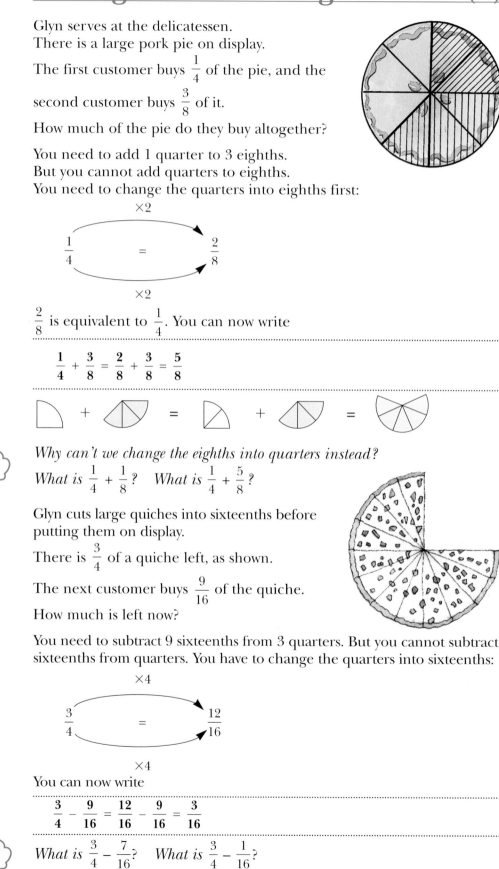

Glyn serves at the delicatessen.
There is a large pork pie on display.

The first customer buys $\frac{1}{4}$ of the pie, and the

second customer buys $\frac{3}{8}$ of it.

How much of the pie do they buy altogether?

You need to add 1 quarter to 3 eighths.
But you cannot add quarters to eighths.
You need to change the quarters into eighths first:

$$\frac{1}{4} \xrightarrow{\times 2}{} = \frac{2}{8} \xleftarrow{\times 2}{}$$

$\frac{2}{8}$ is equivalent to $\frac{1}{4}$. You can now write

$$\frac{1}{4} + \frac{3}{8} = \frac{2}{8} + \frac{3}{8} = \frac{5}{8}$$

Why can't we change the eighths into quarters instead?
What is $\frac{1}{4} + \frac{1}{8}$?   What is $\frac{1}{4} + \frac{5}{8}$?

Glyn cuts large quiches into sixteenths before
putting them on display.

There is $\frac{3}{4}$ of a quiche left, as shown.

The next customer buys $\frac{9}{16}$ of the quiche.

How much is left now?

You need to subtract 9 sixteenths from 3 quarters. But you cannot subtract
sixteenths from quarters. You have to change the quarters into sixteenths:

$$\frac{3}{4} \xrightarrow{\times 4}{} = \frac{12}{16} \xleftarrow{\times 4}{}$$

You can now write

$$\frac{3}{4} - \frac{9}{16} = \frac{12}{16} - \frac{9}{16} = \frac{3}{16}$$

What is $\frac{3}{4} - \frac{7}{16}$?   What is $\frac{3}{4} - \frac{1}{16}$?

Fractions

1 Find the missing number in each of these.

a) $\dfrac{1}{2} = \dfrac{?}{4}$

b) $\dfrac{1}{3} = \dfrac{?}{6}$

c) $\dfrac{6}{8} = \dfrac{3}{?}$

d) $\dfrac{10}{15} = \dfrac{2}{?}$

e) $\dfrac{1}{4} = \dfrac{?}{12}$

f) $\dfrac{6}{9} = \dfrac{2}{?}$

g) $\dfrac{3}{4} = \dfrac{?}{16}$

h) $\dfrac{6}{10} = \dfrac{?}{5}$

i) $\dfrac{30}{40} = \dfrac{3}{?}$

j) $\dfrac{7}{8} = \dfrac{?}{16}$

k) $\dfrac{1}{6} = \dfrac{?}{30}$

l) $\dfrac{7}{10} = \dfrac{21}{?}$

2 This map shows the distance, in miles, from the crossroads to each of 4 buildings.

Work out the distance from
a) Martha's house to the shop
b) Aron's house to the shop
c) Martha's house to Aron's house
d) Martha's house to the railway station.

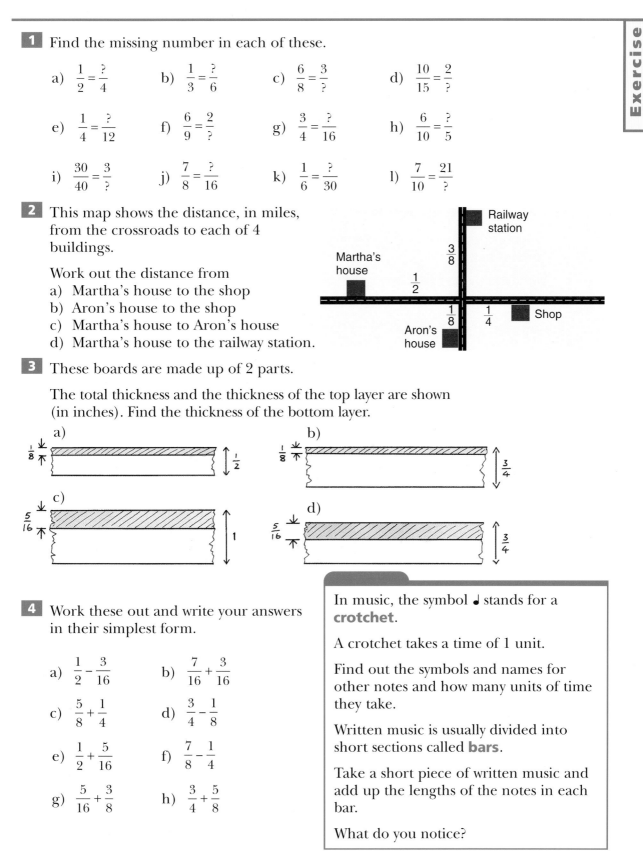

3 These boards are made up of 2 parts.

The total thickness and the thickness of the top layer are shown (in inches). Find the thickness of the bottom layer.

a)

b)

c)

d)

4 Work these out and write your answers in their simplest form.

a) $\dfrac{1}{2} - \dfrac{3}{16}$

b) $\dfrac{7}{16} + \dfrac{3}{16}$

c) $\dfrac{5}{8} + \dfrac{1}{4}$

d) $\dfrac{3}{4} - \dfrac{1}{8}$

e) $\dfrac{1}{2} + \dfrac{5}{16}$

f) $\dfrac{7}{8} - \dfrac{1}{4}$

g) $\dfrac{5}{16} + \dfrac{3}{8}$

h) $\dfrac{3}{4} + \dfrac{5}{8}$

In music, the symbol ♩ stands for a **crotchet**.

A crotchet takes a time of 1 unit.

Find out the symbols and names for other notes and how many units of time they take.

Written music is usually divided into short sections called **bars**.

Take a short piece of written music and add up the lengths of the notes in each bar.

What do you notice?

Improper fractions and mixed numbers

Clare is a waitress.
She is serving apple pie to 7 people.
Each serving is a quarter of a pie.
How many pies does Clare use?

Clare uses 7 quarters ($\frac{7}{4}$).

$\frac{7}{4}$ is an **improper fraction**.

(Some people call it a **'top heavy'** fraction.)

The 7 quarters can be arranged to make 1 whole pie and 3 quarters of a pie.

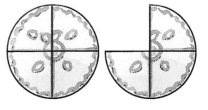

You can see that Clare uses $1\frac{3}{4}$ pies.

$1\frac{3}{4}$ is a **mixed number**. You can write $\frac{7}{4} = 1\frac{3}{4}$.

How many pies does Clare need for 9 people?
She needs 9 quarters, $\frac{9}{4}$.

To see how many whole pies this is, we need to write it as a mixed number.
You divide the top (9) by the bottom (4):

$9 \div 4 = 2$ remainder 1.

This is the number of whole pies.

So $\frac{9}{4} = 2\frac{1}{4}$.

This is the number of extra quarters.

Clare needs $2\frac{1}{4}$ pies.

How many pies do 10 people need?

How many people will $3\frac{3}{4}$ pies serve?

You need to know how many quarters there are in $3\frac{3}{4}$.

$3 \times 4 = 12$

Each whole pie is 4 quarters, so 3 whole pies is 12 quarters $\left(\frac{12}{4}\right)$.

You can write

$$3\frac{3}{4} = 3 + \frac{3}{4} = \frac{12}{4} + \frac{3}{4} = \frac{15}{4}$$

You can see that $3\frac{3}{4}$ is 15 quarters, so it is 15 servings.

Fractions

1 Change these improper fractions to mixed numbers.

    a) $\dfrac{5}{4}$ b) $\dfrac{8}{3}$ c) $\dfrac{3}{2}$ d) $\dfrac{11}{4}$

    e) $\dfrac{13}{8}$ f) $\dfrac{9}{2}$ g) $\dfrac{11}{6}$ h) $\dfrac{12}{3}$

2 Change these mixed numbers to improper fractions.

    a) $3\dfrac{1}{2}$ b) $1\dfrac{5}{8}$ c) $2\dfrac{3}{5}$ d) $3\dfrac{1}{3}$

    e) $4\dfrac{3}{4}$ f) $1\dfrac{3}{16}$ g) $2\dfrac{5}{8}$ h) $6\dfrac{1}{4}$

3 Brian works at a health centre. He sees 7 people for half an hour each. How many hours does it take him?

4 Tess records 13 programmes each lasting quarter of an hour. How many hours does it take?

5 The bottles of mineral water in this pack each contain $\dfrac{1}{2}$ litre.

How many litres of water does the pack contain?

6 A doctor has a $2\dfrac{1}{2}$ hour clinic. How many $\dfrac{1}{2}$ hour appointments can be fitted in?

7 Joanna has $2\dfrac{3}{4}$ hours left of a videotape.

How many $\dfrac{1}{4}$ hour programmes can she record?

8 Parvez is a chef. He allows 1 kg of rice for 8 people.

How many people can he serve with $2\dfrac{1}{4}$ kg?

9 Bottles of wine are packed in boxes of 6. Diana has $3\dfrac{1}{2}$ boxes.

How many bottles of wine does Diana have?

Keep a record of how long you spend watching television for each of the seven days of a week.

Give each day's total to the nearest $\dfrac{1}{4}$ hour (for example, $1\dfrac{3}{4}$ hours). How much television did you watch in the whole week?

Mixed numbers

Thomas wants to record two programmes on video.

The Match lasts $1\frac{3}{4}$ hours. Star Trek lasts $1\frac{1}{2}$ hours.

How much videotape time does he need?

You find the total time by adding $1\frac{3}{4}$ and $1\frac{1}{2}$.

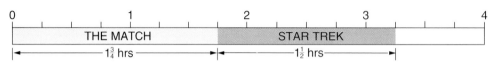

This is shown on the diagram above, but you can do it without drawing a diagram.

First add the whole numbers: $1 + 1 = 2$

Then add the fractions: $\frac{3}{4} + \frac{1}{2} = \frac{3}{4} + \frac{2}{4}$

The whole numbers.

You have to change the half into quarters before you can add them.

$$= \frac{5}{4} = 1\frac{1}{4}$$

So $1\frac{3}{4} + 1\frac{1}{2} = 2 + 1\frac{1}{4} = 3\frac{1}{4}$

The fractions.

Thomas needs $3\frac{1}{4}$ hours videotape time.

Sam has $2\frac{3}{4}$ hours left unused on a videotape.

She records $1\frac{1}{2}$ hours of MTV.

How much time will be left?

You find this by taking $1\frac{1}{2}$ away from $2\frac{3}{4}$.

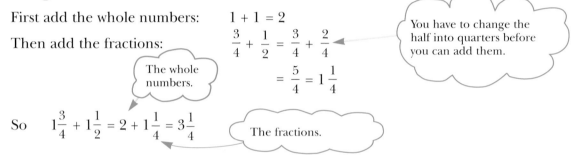

tape already used

$2\frac{3}{4} - 1\frac{1}{2} = 1\frac{1}{4}$ hrs

This is shown on the diagram above but you can do it without drawing a diagram.

First subtract the whole numbers: $2 - 1 = 1$

Then subtract the fractions: $\frac{3}{4} - \frac{1}{2} = \frac{3}{4} - \frac{2}{4} = \frac{1}{4}$

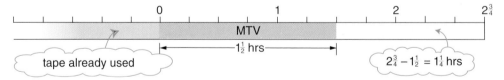

So $2\frac{3}{4} - 1\frac{1}{2} = 1 + \frac{1}{4} = 1\frac{1}{4}$

The whole numbers.

The fractions.

Sam has $1\frac{1}{4}$ hours left on her tape.

1 a) $2\frac{1}{2}+1\frac{3}{4}$ b) $1\frac{5}{8}+\frac{7}{8}$ c) $1\frac{5}{8}-\frac{1}{4}$

d) $1\frac{3}{4}+2\frac{5}{8}$ e) $1\frac{1}{2}-\frac{3}{16}$ f) $\frac{3}{8}+2$

g) $2-\frac{1}{4}$ h) $3\frac{1}{2}-\frac{3}{4}$ i) $4\frac{1}{2}-1\frac{7}{8}$

2 This map shows the distances, in miles, between 5 villages.

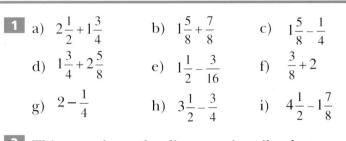

a) What is the distance from Benton to Ditton?
b) What is the distance from Ashley to Cowley?
c) What is the distance from Cowley to Elton?
d) Use your answers to b) and c) to find the distance from Ashley to Elton.

3 Philip's train journey is expected to take $2\frac{3}{4}$ hours.

The train is delayed for $\frac{1}{2}$ hour on the way.

How long does the journey take?

4 Brass is made from copper and zinc. In $3\frac{3}{4}$ kilograms of brass there

are $2\frac{1}{4}$ kilograms of copper.

How much zinc is there?

5 A coach journey takes $4\frac{3}{4}$ hours. The same journey by train takes

$3\frac{1}{2}$ hours.

How much time is saved by going by train?

6 The diagram shows a screw holding
2 pieces of wood together. All the
measurements are in inches.

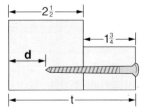

a) Find the total thickness, t inches.

b) The screw is 3 inches long. Find the
distance, d inches between the screw
point and the side of the wood.

Blank videotapes are either 3 hours or
4 hours long.

Which would you use to record several
episodes of

a) a $1\frac{1}{4}$ hour programme?

b) a $1\frac{1}{2}$ hour programme?

c) a programme of your choice (write
down its name and the length of
each episode, too).

Fractions of a quantity

Look at this headline.

Daily Globe

One in four workers to lose jobs

There are 120 workers.

How many will lose their jobs?

1 in 4 is the same as $\frac{1}{4}$ (one quarter).

You need to find $\frac{1}{4}$ of 120.

You can write $\frac{1}{4} \times 120 = 120 \times 1 \div 4$

First multiply by the top number…

You can write 'of' as ×.

$= 120 \div 4$

…then divide by the bottom number.

$= 30$

30 workers lose their jobs.

The next week you see this headline.

Daily Globe

Two thirds of job losers offered new work

30 people lost their jobs: how many are offered new work?

Two thirds of 30 is $\frac{2}{3} \times 30$.

First multiply by the top number…

$\frac{2}{3} \times 30 = 30 \times 2 \div 3$

$= 60 \div 3$

…then divide by the bottom number.

$= 20$

20 people are offered new work.

You may find it easier to find $\frac{2}{3}$ of 30 this way:

First find $\frac{1}{3}$ of 30:

$30 \div 3 = 10$

Then multiply by 2 to get $\frac{2}{3}$ of 30:

$10 \times 2 = 20$

How many are not offered work?

What fraction of the job losers is this?

48

Fractions

1 Work out

a) $\frac{1}{3} \times 18$ b) $\frac{3}{4} \times 8$ c) $\frac{2}{5} \times 100$

d) $\frac{1}{4}$ of 36   e) $\frac{9}{10}$ of 80   f) $\frac{4}{3} \times 30$

2 Holly buys this tent.
How much does she save by buying it in the sale?

£60

SALE
$\frac{1}{3}$ OFF ALL MARKED PRICES

3 24 people apply for a job. One quarter of them get an interview.
How many get an interview?

4 Donna takes her young son Samuel on this coach trip.

a) How much is Samuel's fare?

b) How much does it cost in total?

COACH TOUR
DALES HIGHLIGHTS

ADULTS £6
CHILDREN HALF FARE

5 Anneena's car cost £12 000 when new.

a) It is now worth two thirds of this. How much is it worth now?

b) Since Anneena bought her car, the price of the same model has gone up by a quarter. How much does a new one cost now?

6 Hightown's annual rainfall last year was 96 cm.

a) One sixth ($\frac{1}{6}$) of the rain fell in January. How many cm is this?

b) One eighth ($\frac{1}{8}$) of the rain fell in April. How many cm is this?

7 Last year the sales of a business were £600 000 a year.

In the current year the sales are expected to increase by one third.

What are the expected sales for the current year?

8 There are 50 people at a party. Three fifths of them are female. How many are male?

> Go to your local supermarket and find out whether bulk buys are always better value.
>
> For example, is 10 packets of crisps for £2.40 better than 6 for £1.50?
>
> (You need to work out the price of 1 packet in each case.)

Finishing off

> **Now that you have finished this chapter you should be able to**
>
> ★ find equivalent fractions
>
> ★ find the simplest form of a fraction
>
> ★ add and subtract fractions
>
> ★ change between improper fractions and mixed numbers
>
> ★ find a fraction of a quantity

Use the questions in the next exercise to check that you understand everything.

Mixed exercise

1 In each of these, write the fraction in its simplest form.

a) $\dfrac{12}{16}$ b) $\dfrac{10}{40}$ c) $\dfrac{15}{25}$ d) $\dfrac{18}{20}$ e) $\dfrac{24}{36}$ f) $\dfrac{25}{100}$

2 In each of these, write the answer in its simplest form.

a) $\dfrac{3}{10}+\dfrac{1}{10}$ b) $\dfrac{3}{16}+\dfrac{11}{16}$ c) $1-\dfrac{3}{5}$ d) $1-\dfrac{5}{8}$

3 Jo is making a fruit salad. She writes this list of the things she needs.

She finds these things in the fruit bowl.

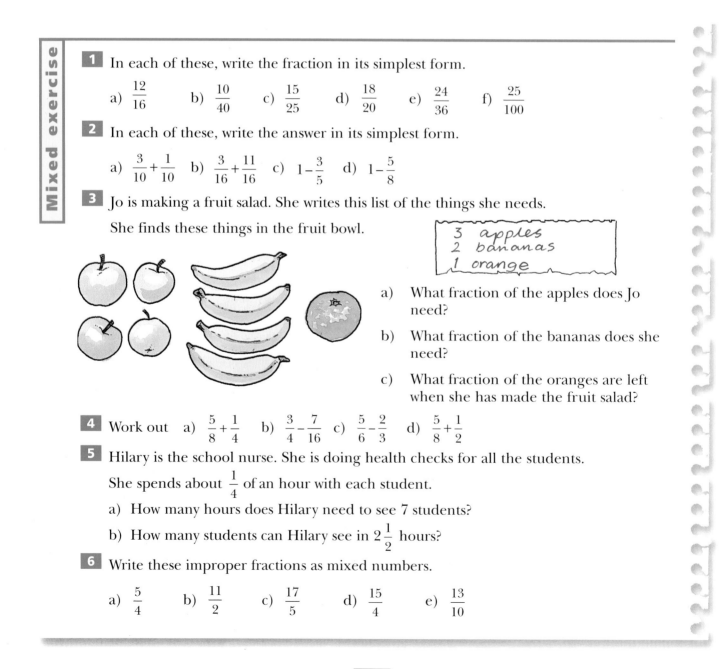

3 apples
2 bananas
1 orange

a) What fraction of the apples does Jo need?

b) What fraction of the bananas does she need?

c) What fraction of the oranges are left when she has made the fruit salad?

4 Work out   a) $\dfrac{5}{8}+\dfrac{1}{4}$ b) $\dfrac{3}{4}-\dfrac{7}{16}$ c) $\dfrac{5}{6}-\dfrac{2}{3}$ d) $\dfrac{5}{8}+\dfrac{1}{2}$

5 Hilary is the school nurse. She is doing health checks for all the students.

She spends about $\dfrac{1}{4}$ of an hour with each student.

a) How many hours does Hilary need to see 7 students?

b) How many students can Hilary see in $2\dfrac{1}{2}$ hours?

6 Write these improper fractions as mixed numbers.

a) $\dfrac{5}{4}$ b) $\dfrac{11}{2}$ c) $\dfrac{17}{5}$ d) $\dfrac{15}{4}$ e) $\dfrac{13}{10}$

7 Write these mixed numbers as improper fractions.

a) $4\frac{1}{2}$　　b) $3\frac{3}{4}$　　c) $2\frac{7}{8}$　　d) $1\frac{9}{10}$　　e) $2\frac{1}{5}$

8 Lyn is orienteering. Here is her map.

She has reached Checkpoint 2.

a) What distance has she travelled?

b) How far has she still to go?

c) What distance will she have travelled when she reaches the finish?

9 Work these out and write your answers in their simplest forms.

a) $2\frac{1}{2} + \frac{3}{4}$　　b) $2 - \frac{5}{8}$　　c) $1\frac{5}{8} + 1\frac{1}{2}$　　d) $1\frac{3}{4} + 3\frac{3}{8}$

e) $\frac{1}{4} + 2\frac{7}{8}$　　f) $3\frac{5}{6} + 2\frac{1}{6}$　　g) $2\frac{3}{16} - \frac{5}{8}$　　h) $4\frac{1}{4} - 2\frac{3}{4}$

10 Jack's water butt holds 180 litres.

The first picture shows the butt before Jack waters his plants.

The second picture shows the butt after he has watered the plants.

a) How much water is in the butt before he starts?

b) How much water is in the butt when he has finished?

c) How much water has he used?

(Write your answers in litres.)

11 Here are the carriages of an Intercity train.

Buffet

a) What fraction of the train is First class (1)?

b) What fraction of the train is buffet?

c) What fraction is Standard class (unmarked)?

d) Check that these fractions add up to 1.

Take a standard 12-inch ruler and look at the scales for inches.

What lengths between 0 and 1 inch can you measure exactly?

(Give your answers as fractions of an inch, for example $\frac{7}{10}$ inch.)

Six

Maps and drawings

Maps and scales

This is a map of the village of Greenbridge.

It shows some of the main buildings in the village, and the homes of three families, the Whites, the Greens and the Browns.

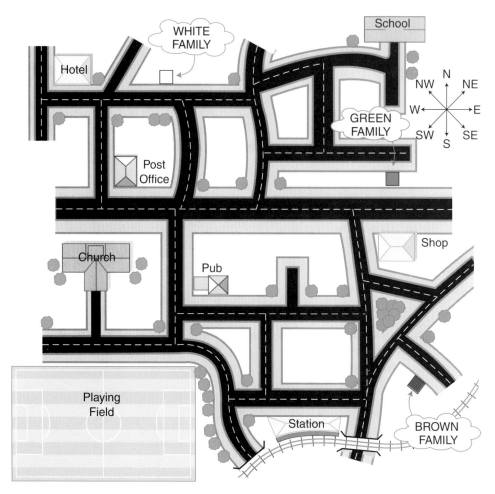

The **scale** of this map is 1 cm to 10 metres. This means that 1 cm on the map stands for 10 metres in real life.

Every map needs a scale.

The length of the playing field on the map is 5 cm.

As each centimetre stands for 10 metres in real life, the playing field must be 50 metres long.

Measure the width of the playing field on the map.

How wide is the field in real life?

For questions 1 to 8, use the map of Greenbridge opposite.

1 a) Which family lives north of the shop?

b) Which building is south-east of the Post Office?

c) Which building is north-east of the pub?

d) Which family lives furthest west?

2 What direction must a crow fly in to go directly from

a) the Whites' house to the hotel?

b) the Browns' house to the Whites' house?

c) the school to the playing field?

d) the Greens' house to the shop?

3 The church is south-west of the school.

In which direction is the school from the church?

4 Mrs White turns left out of her house. She takes the second right, then the second left. She stops just past the first turning on the right.

What building has she reached?

5 Mr Green uses the train every morning to go to work.

Give directions for him to get from his home to the station.

6 A visitor arrives at the station and wants to go to the hotel.

What directions would you give her?

7 a) Measure the distance on the map from the Post Office to the village shop.

b) How far would this distance be in real life?

8 Jessica Brown, Mark Green and Ryan White all attend the village school.

a) Who do you think has the shortest walk to school?

b) Measure the distance that each has to walk. (You could use a piece of string or the edge of a piece of paper to make this easier.)

c) Work out how far each child has to walk in real life.

Measure a room at home using paces.

Draw a plan view of the room and its main contents using a scale of 1 cm to 1 pace.

Scales

The map of Greenbridge had a scale of 1 cm to 10 metres.

This map is part of an Ordnance Survey map of South Devon.

Its scale is 1:50 000.

This means that 1 unit on the map stands for 50 000 units in real life.

For example, 1 cm on the map is 50 000 cm in real life.

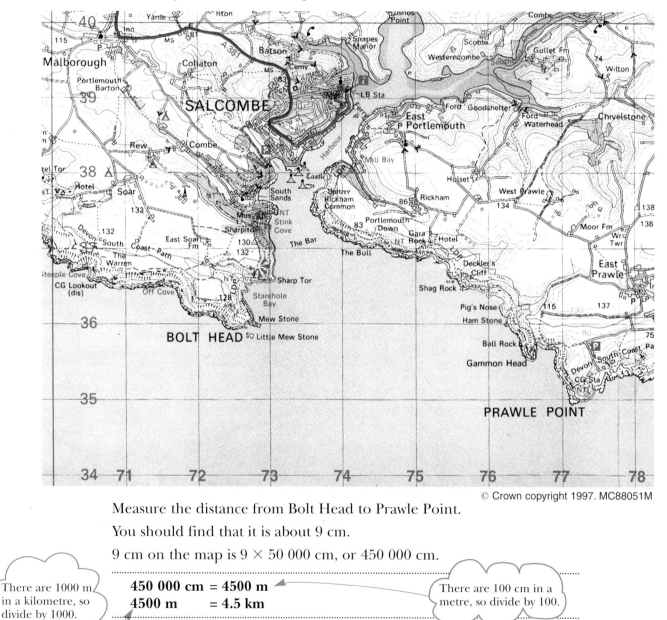

© Crown copyright 1997. MC88051M

Measure the distance from Bolt Head to Prawle Point.

You should find that it is about 9 cm.

9 cm on the map is 9 × 50 000 cm, or 450 000 cm.

There are 1000 m in a kilometre, so divide by 1000.

There are 100 cm in a metre, so divide by 100.

450 000 cm = 4500 m
4500 m   = 4.5 km

So the distance from Bolt Head to Prawle Point is 4.5 km in real life.

It is easier to find things on the map if you use grid references.

The village of West Prawle is in grid square 76 37

This is the grid line at the left of the square.

This is the grid line underneath the square.

1 A map is drawn to a scale of 1:25 000. How far in real life are these distances on the map? (Give your answers in metres.)

   a) 1 cm   b) 6 cm   c) 8 mm   d) 3 mm   e) 9.5 mm

For questions 2 to 4, use the map of the Salcombe area opposite.

2 a) Measure, in centimetres, the width of one grid square on the map.
   b) How many centimetres is this in real life?
   c) How many metres is it?
   d) How many kilometres is it?

3 Find where the ferry crosses the estuary (square 7438).

   a) Measure, in millimetres, the distance that the ferry travels.
   b) How far is this in real life?

4 Find Moor Farm in square 7737.

   Use string or the edge of a piece of paper to measure the distance by road to the church in East Portlemouth.

   How far is this in real life?

5 Here are the plans of the ground floor and first floor of a house.

   The scale of the drawings is 1:150.

Write a description of the house, giving the length and width of each room in metres.

Using a scale of 1 cm to 1 m, make a plan of the ground floor of your home.

Angles

A robot is being programmed to travel along this path.

The scale is 1 cm to 2 m.

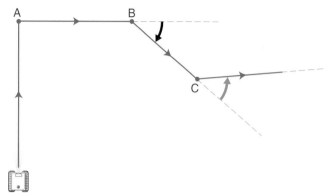

The first 3 instructions are   GO FORWARD 8 METRES
                                                TURN RIGHT THROUGH A QUARTER TURN
                                                GO FORWARD 6 METRES

The robot is now at point B. It needs to turn again.

This time it is not a quarter turn. It is less than that.

The robot needs to be told what **angle** to turn through.

Angles are measured in **degrees**. You need an **angle measurer** or a **protractor** to measure an angle.

Measure the angle the robot needs to turn. It is shown by the red arrow.

You should find that the angle is 40 degrees. This is written as 40°.

Types of angle

A whole turn is 360°, so a half turn is 180° and a quarter turn is 90°.

An angle of 90° is called a **right angle**.

An angle less than 90° is called an **acute angle**.

An angle bigger than 90° but smaller than 180° (between a quarter turn and a half turn) is called an **obtuse angle**.

An angle bigger than 180° (between a half turn and a whole turn) is called a **reflex angle**.

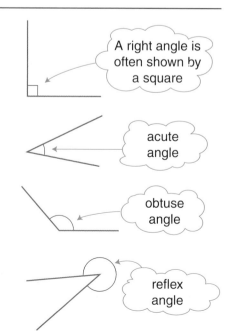

A right angle is often shown by a square

acute angle

obtuse angle

reflex angle

1 For each of these angles, say (without measuring) whether it is an acute angle, a right angle, an obtuse angle or a reflex angle.

a

b

c

d

e

f

2 Estimate each of the angles in question 1.

3 Measure each of the angles in question 1 and see how good your estimates were.

4 Look again at the robot path on page 56. The instruction for the corner at B was TURN RIGHT 40°.
Write the next 2 instructions for the robot.

You are designing a company logo.

Write a set of instructions to cut the logo from a large sheet of vinyl. Use the commands
FORWARD (and a distance)
          e.g. FORWARD 30 cm
RIGHT   (and an angle)
          e.g. RIGHT 90°
LEFT   (and an angle)
          e.g. LEFT 45°.

Your logo should be made up of straight lines.

Draw the logo accurately using the scale of your choice.

Finishing off

Now that you have finished this chapter you should

- ★ be able to follow and give directions using a map

- ★ know how to use the scale on a map or scale drawing

- ★ be able to use the 8 compass directions

- ★ know what is meant by a right angle, an acute angle, a reflex angle and an obtuse angle

- ★ be able to use a protractor or angle measurer to measure angles in degrees

Use the questions in the next exercise to check that you understand everything.

Mixed exercise

This map shows part of Edinburgh city centre.

The scale is 1 cm to 125 metres.

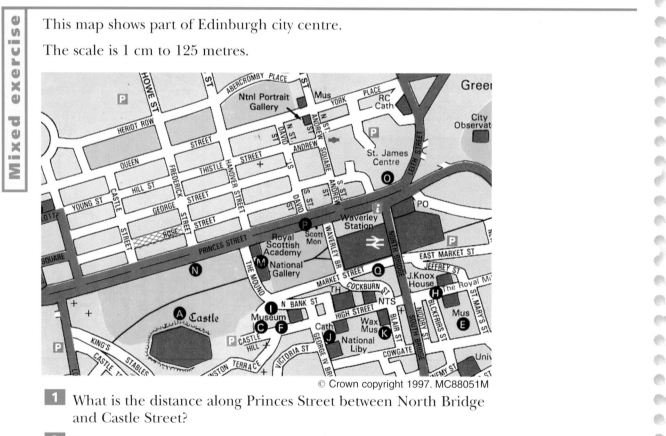

© Crown copyright 1997. MC88051M

1 What is the distance along Princes Street between North Bridge and Castle Street?

2 The Patel family have parked their car at the car park (marked P) by the castle.

a) Give them directions to get to the National Portrait Gallery (north of Waverley station).

b) How far do the Patels have to walk?

3 The diagram shows the route of a sailing race.

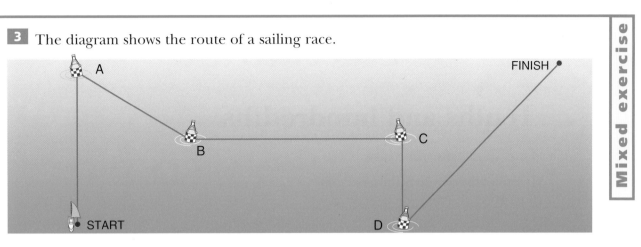

a) Copy and complete the table below.

Stage of race	Distance on map	Distance in real life	Direction
START to A	4 cm	0.8 km	North
A to B			
B to C			
C to D			
D to FINISH			

b) What is the total length of the race course?

4 This is a doll's house.

The scale diagram below shows two of the pieces of wood used for the roof.

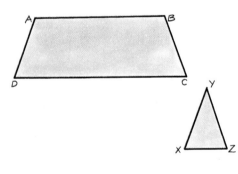

Measure the angles at each corner of the pieces of wood.

Write your answers like this.

Angle BAD = ...

Use a computer to draw the shape that you designed for your company logo on page 57.

Experiment with it to see if you can make it better.

Print out your final design.

Seven

Decimals

Tenths and hundredths

Look at this **number line**.

It shows the whole numbers from 0 to 10.

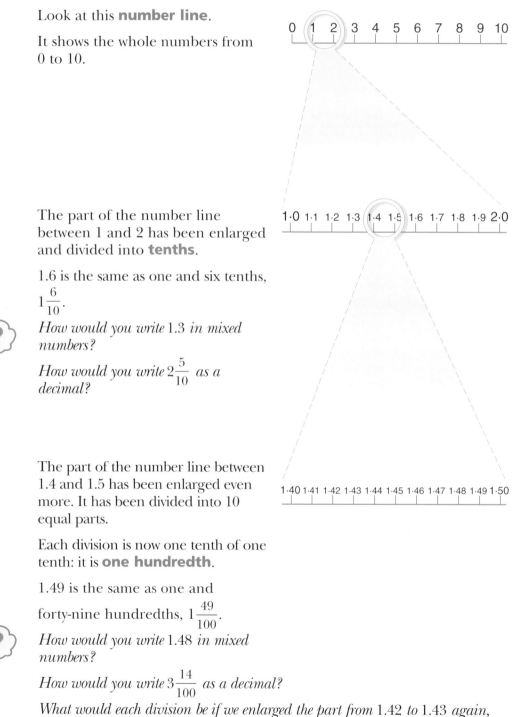

The part of the number line between 1 and 2 has been enlarged and divided into **tenths**.

1.6 is the same as one and six tenths, $1\frac{6}{10}$.

How would you write 1.3 in mixed numbers?

How would you write $2\frac{5}{10}$ as a decimal?

The part of the number line between 1.4 and 1.5 has been enlarged even more. It has been divided into 10 equal parts.

Each division is now one tenth of one tenth: it is **one hundredth**.

1.49 is the same as one and forty-nine hundredths, $1\frac{49}{100}$.

How would you write 1.48 in mixed numbers?

How would you write $3\frac{14}{100}$ as a decimal?

What would each division be if we enlarged the part from 1.42 to 1.43 again, and divided it into 10 equal parts?

1 Look at this number line.

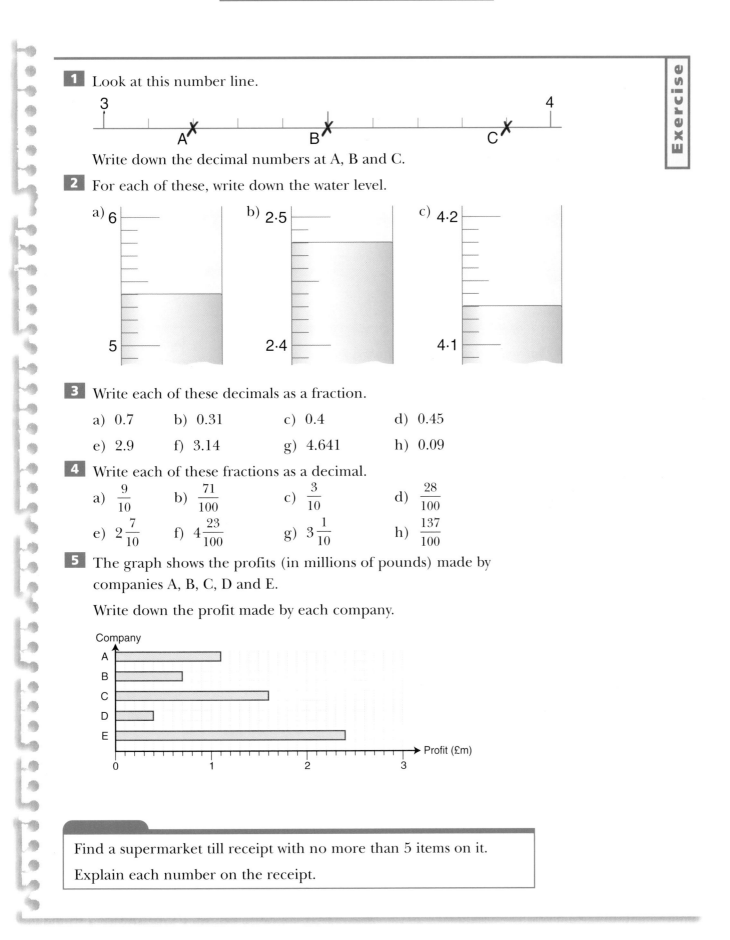

Write down the decimal numbers at A, B and C.

2 For each of these, write down the water level.

a)

b)

c)

3 Write each of these decimals as a fraction.

a) 0.7   b) 0.31   c) 0.4   d) 0.45

e) 2.9   f) 3.14   g) 4.641   h) 0.09

4 Write each of these fractions as a decimal.

a) $\dfrac{9}{10}$ b) $\dfrac{71}{100}$ c) $\dfrac{3}{10}$ d) $\dfrac{28}{100}$

e) $2\dfrac{7}{10}$ f) $4\dfrac{23}{100}$ g) $3\dfrac{1}{10}$ h) $\dfrac{137}{100}$

5 The graph shows the profits (in millions of pounds) made by companies A, B, C, D and E.

Write down the profit made by each company.

Find a supermarket till receipt with no more than 5 items on it.

Explain each number on the receipt.

Halves and quarters

Look at this number line from 0 to 1.

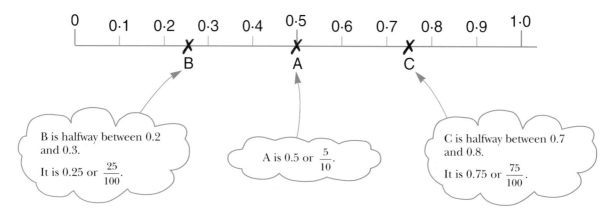

0   0.1   0.2   0.3   0.4   0.5   0.6   0.7   0.8   0.9   1.0

X   X   X
B   A   C

B is halfway between 0.2 and 0.3.

It is 0.25 or $\frac{25}{100}$.

A is 0.5 or $\frac{5}{10}$.

C is halfway between 0.7 and 0.8.

It is 0.75 or $\frac{75}{100}$.

 Write each of the fractions in its simplest form.

Check that you agree with the numbers in this table.

How would you write $2\frac{3}{4}$ in decimals?

Fraction	Decimal
$\frac{1}{4}$	0.25
$\frac{1}{2}$	0.50
$\frac{3}{4}$	0.75

Fifths

Look at the number line from 0 to 1 below. It is divided into tenths (but they are not all labelled).

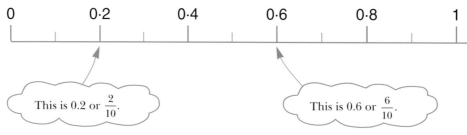

0   0.2   0.4   0.6   0.8   1

This is 0.2 or $\frac{2}{10}$.

This is 0.6 or $\frac{6}{10}$.

 Write each of the fractions in its simplest form.

Check that you agree with the numbers in this table.

How would you write $3\frac{2}{5}$ in decimals?

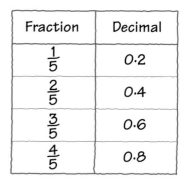

Fraction	Decimal
$\frac{1}{5}$	0.2
$\frac{2}{5}$	0.4
$\frac{3}{5}$	0.6
$\frac{4}{5}$	0.8

Decimals

1 Write these fractions as decimals.

a) $2\frac{1}{4}$ b) $3\frac{1}{2}$ c) $5\frac{3}{4}$ d) $1\frac{1}{2}$

e) $3\frac{3}{4}$ f) $7\frac{1}{4}$ g) $6\frac{1}{2}$ h) $1\frac{3}{4}$

i) $\frac{4}{5}$ j) $1\frac{3}{5}$ k) $3\frac{1}{5}$ l) $2\frac{2}{5}$

2 Write these decimals as fractions or mixed numbers, in their simplest form.

a) 4.5 b) 3.25 c) 2.75 d) 8.5

e) 1.25 f) 5.5 g) 4.75 h) 6.25

i) 0.6 j) 1.4 k) 2.8 l) 3.2

3 This number line from 4 to 5 has been divided into tenths.

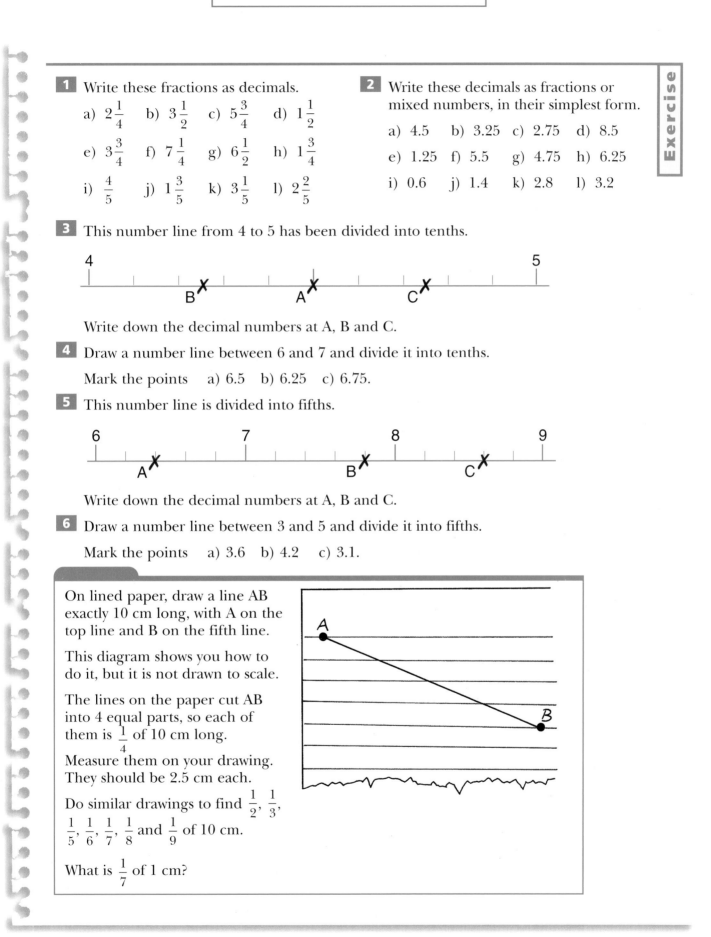

Write down the decimal numbers at A, B and C.

4 Draw a number line between 6 and 7 and divide it into tenths.

Mark the points   a) 6.5   b) 6.25   c) 6.75.

5 This number line is divided into fifths.

Write down the decimal numbers at A, B and C.

6 Draw a number line between 3 and 5 and divide it into fifths.

Mark the points   a) 3.6   b) 4.2   c) 3.1.

On lined paper, draw a line AB exactly 10 cm long, with A on the top line and B on the fifth line.

This diagram shows you how to do it, but it is not drawn to scale.

The lines on the paper cut AB into 4 equal parts, so each of them is $\frac{1}{4}$ of 10 cm long.

Measure them on your drawing. They should be 2.5 cm each.

Do similar drawings to find $\frac{1}{2}$, $\frac{1}{3}$, $\frac{1}{5}$, $\frac{1}{6}$, $\frac{1}{7}$, $\frac{1}{8}$ and $\frac{1}{9}$ of 10 cm.

What is $\frac{1}{7}$ of 1 cm?

Adding and subtracting decimals

Every time you add and subtract amounts of money you are working with decimals.

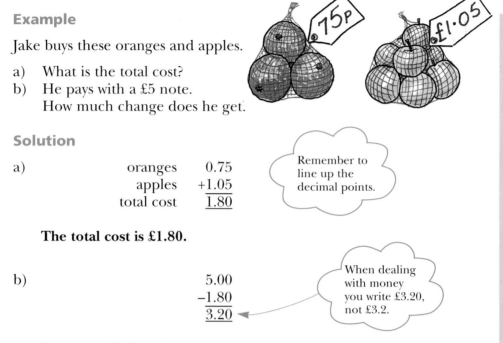

Example

Jake buys these oranges and apples.

a)   What is the total cost?
b)   He pays with a £5 note.
     How much change does he get.

Solution

a)
$$
\begin{array}{rr}
\text{oranges} & 0.75 \\
\text{apples} & +1.05 \\
\hline
\text{total cost} & 1.80 \\
\hline
\end{array}
$$

Remember to line up the decimal points.

The total cost is £1.80.

b)
$$
\begin{array}{r}
5.00 \\
-1.80 \\
\hline
3.20 \\
\hline
\end{array}
$$

When dealing with money you write £3.20, not £3.2.

Jake gets £3.20 change.

Here is a plan of Ann's lounge-diner.

Ann wants to know the length of the room.

She works it out like this:

$$
\begin{array}{r}
3 \cdot 60 \\
+ 2 \cdot 25 \\
\hline
5 \cdot 85 \\
\hline
\end{array}
$$

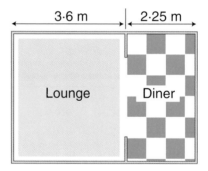

3·6 m   2·25 m

Lounge   Diner

 Why did Ann write 3.6 as 3.60?

The lounge-diner is 5.85 m long.

Ann's mother has given her a carpet 8 m long for her lounge-diner.
Ann wants to know how much will be left over.
She works it out like this:

$$
\begin{array}{r}
8 \cdot 00 \\
- 5 \cdot 85 \\
\hline
2 \cdot 15 \\
\hline
\end{array}
$$

 Why does Ann write 8 as 8.00?

Ann has 2.15 m of carpet left.

1 Work out the answers to these.

  a) £1.10   b) £7.60   c) £3.55
     + £2.45   + £1.30   + £2.60

  d) £10.20 e) £6.54   f) £7.15
     − £2.10   − £6.42   − £4.20

2 Work out the answers to these.

  a) 1.6 + 3.2   b) 4.8 + 3.12

  c) 10.6 + 10.43 d) 4.9 − 3.01

  e) 4.01 − 3.8   f) 5.51 − 3.8

3 Kieran buys a T-shirt for £6.99.

How much change does he get from a £10 note?

4 Sara is a waitress.

She takes this order from Table 3.

Work out the bill for Table 3.

Table 3
Fish & chips £4·25
Chicken & chips £4·55
Pot of tea £0·85
Coffee £0·70

5 Woods 1·7 km

Kate walks to the woods.
She passes the sign on the left.

Some time later she passes the sign on the right.

How far has she walked in this time?

Woods 0·25 km

6 Phil's lorry is 4.6 m high.

How much clearance will there be if he drives under this bridge?

(The clearance is the space between the bridge and the lorry.)

5·3m

Use the price list from your canteen or a local take-away.

Write down a lunch order for yourself and a friend.

List each item and its price.

Work out the total cost.

How much change would you get if you paid with a £20 note?

Multiples of 10

Leo has 10 glasses to fill with water.
Each glass has a capacity of 0.25 litres.
How much water does Leo need?

You need to work out 0.25×10.
To multiply a decimal by 10, you move the decimal point 1 place to the right:

$$0.25 \times 10 = 02.5$$

We usually leave out the zero and write this as 2.5

 What is 0.75×10?
What is 0.4×10?
What is 4.3×10?

How many litres would Leo need to fill 100 of these glasses?

You need to work out 0.25×100.
To multiply a decimal by 100, you move the decimal point 2 places to the right:

$$0.25 \times 100 = 025.$$

We usually leave out the zero and the decimal point, and write this as 25

Leo needs 25 litres of water.

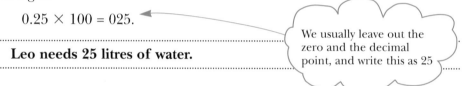 *What is 0.75×100?*
What is 0.4×100?

What is the rule for multiplying by 1000?

Leo has 2.5 litres of water to divide equally between 10 glasses.
How much water should he put in each glass?

You have already seen that to put 0.25 litres in each of 10 glasses you need 2.5 litres.

So Leo should put 0.25 litres in each glass.

You can write

$$2.5 \div 10 = 0.25$$

$\div 10$
2.5 becomes .25

You can see that to divide by 10 you move the decimal point 1 place to the left.

 What is $7.5 \div 10$?
What is $4 \div 10$?

To divide by 100 you move the decimal point 2 places to the left.

 How do you divide by 1000?

Decimals

1 Work out

a) 1.6×10 b) 3.01×10 c) 21.0×10

d) 0.35×100 e) 7.6×100 f) 0.032×100

2 Ayla orders 15 boxes of computer disks. Each box contains 10 disks. How many disks does she order?

3 a) How much do 10 of these pens cost?

b) How much do 100 cost?

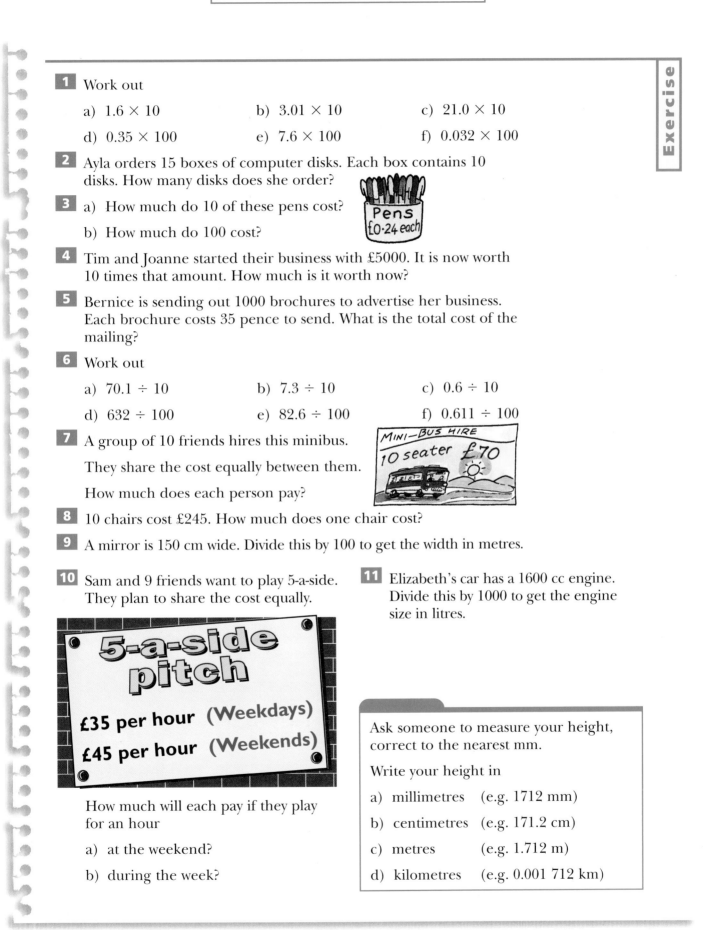

Pens £0·24 each

4 Tim and Joanne started their business with £5000. It is now worth 10 times that amount. How much is it worth now?

5 Bernice is sending out 1000 brochures to advertise her business. Each brochure costs 35 pence to send. What is the total cost of the mailing?

6 Work out

a) $70.1 \div 10$ b) $7.3 \div 10$ c) $0.6 \div 10$

d) $632 \div 100$ e) $82.6 \div 100$ f) $0.611 \div 100$

7 A group of 10 friends hires this minibus.

They share the cost equally between them.

How much does each person pay?

MINI–BUS HIRE
10 seater £70

8 10 chairs cost £245. How much does one chair cost?

9 A mirror is 150 cm wide. Divide this by 100 to get the width in metres.

10 Sam and 9 friends want to play 5-a-side. They plan to share the cost equally.

11 Elizabeth's car has a 1600 cc engine. Divide this by 1000 to get the engine size in litres.

5-a-side pitch

£35 per hour (Weekdays)
£45 per hour (Weekends)

How much will each pay if they play for an hour

a) at the weekend?

b) during the week?

Ask someone to measure your height, correct to the nearest mm.

Write your height in

a) millimetres (e.g. 1712 mm)

b) centimetres (e.g. 171.2 cm)

c) metres (e.g. 1.712 m)

d) kilometres (e.g. 0.001 712 km)

Multiplying decimals

Martine works in catering.

Her purchases and her recipes are not always in the same units.

She needs to work out how many pounds there are in 5 kg of potatoes.
She knows that 1 kg is 2.2 pounds.

This is what Martine writes down.

5 kg is 5 X 2·2 lb

5 X 22 = 110

So 5kg = 11·0 lb

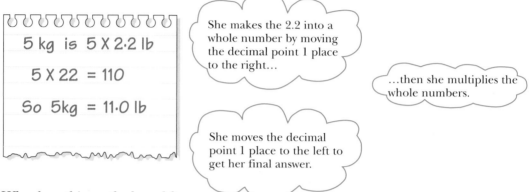

She makes the 2.2 into a whole number by moving the decimal point 1 place to the right…

…then she multiplies the whole numbers.

She moves the decimal point 1 place to the left to get her final answer.

 Why does this method work?

Martine needs to work out how many litres there are in 4.5 pints of milk. She knows that 1 pint is 0.57 litres.

She writes it like this:

4·5 pints is 4·5 X 0·57 litres
45 X 57 = 2565
So 4·5 pints = 2·565 litres

You met squares in Chapter 3. You know that 4 squared is written 4^2 and means 4×4.

You square decimals in the same way.

For example, 3.2 squared is written 3.2^2 and means 3.2×3.2.

 Use the x^2 key on your calculator to work out 3.2^2. (You should get 10.24.)

When you have to multiply a decimal by a nice round number (such as 50 or 400) you can do it quickly by hand.

For example,   £12.50 $\times$ 50 = £12.50 $\times$ 10 $\times$ 5

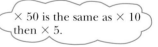

$\times$ 50 is the same as $\times$ 10 then $\times$ 5.

= £125.00 $\times$ 5 = £625.00

 How much does it cost a company to give its 400 employees a £10.50 bottle of champagne each at Christmas?

1 Work out the answers to these.

a) 2×3.6 b) 4×1.5 c) 8×1.11 d) 5×0.16

e) 3×0.04 f) 7×1.04 g) 2×0.031 h) 9×10.6

2 The table shows the heights of 4 children on their second birthdays. To estimate the height that each child will reach when fully grown, you double the height at age 2.

Copy this table and complete it by working out the estimated fully grown heights.

Name	Height at age 2 (m)	Fully grown height (m)
Amy	0.85	
Jack	0.83	
Ryan	0.96	
Laura	0.89	

3 The map shows the route of a cycle race. Distances are in kilometres.

Using the fact that 1 kilometre is about 0.6 miles, write the distances in miles.

Set out your answers like this.

Guiseley $\longrightarrow$ Bingley : 8km = 8 X 0·6 miles = ...

4 a) How much would 2 sessions on this sunbed cost?

b) How much would 5 sessions on the sunbed cost?

c) Is the price for 10 sessions good value?

SUNBED

| 1 session | £1.75 |
| 10 sessions | £15.75 |

5 Work out the square of

a) 1.5   b) 2.2   c) 0.5   d) 4.8

6 Work out

a) 200×4.5 b) 8.3×30

c) 0.5×700 d) 4000×2.5

e) 400×25 f) 0.06×300

g) 0.01×2000 h) 500×10.1

In the UK, road atlases and signs have distances in miles.

A mile is about 1.6 kilometres, so to convert miles to km you multiply by 1.6.

This chart shows the distances between 5 major UK cities.

Copy the chart, but write all the distances in km.

Glasgow is 291 miles from Birmingham

Birmingham				
108	Cardiff			
284	367	Edinburgh		
291	393	46	Glasgow	
120	155	372	403	London

7 A rock concert is sold out: 20 000 people have bought tickets at £13.50 each. How much have they paid altogether?

Dividing decimals

Dan is ordering headed notepaper at £31.50 for 5 reams.

Dan needs to know the price per ream.

This is what he writes.

He is careful to put this decimal point in line with the one below it.

 Another supplier charges £28.80 for 4 reams.

Is this a better buy?

Gloria is ordering fruit juice for a training course.

One supplier sells 1.5-litre bottles at £1.20 each.

Gloria needs to work out the price per litre.

This is what she writes.

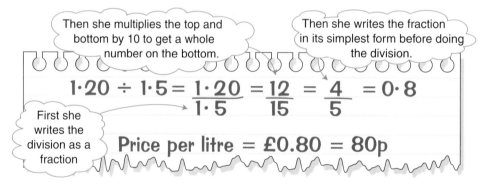

Then she multiplies the top and bottom by 10 to get a whole number on the bottom.

Then she writes the fraction in its simplest form before doing the division.

First she writes the division as a fraction

$$1{\cdot}20 \div 1{\cdot}5 = \frac{1{\cdot}20}{1{\cdot}5} = \frac{12}{15} = \frac{4}{5} = 0{\cdot}8$$

Price per litre = £0.80 = 80p

 Another company sells 2.5-litre bottles of juice at £1.90.

Is this a better buy?

Square roots

You met square roots in Chapter 3. You know, for example, that the square root of 36 (written $\sqrt{36}$) is 6.

$6^2 = 36$ so $\sqrt{36} = 6$.

For most numbers, you need a calculator to work out the square root.

Check that you can find the square root of 10.24 with your calculator. (You should get 3.2.)

Decimals

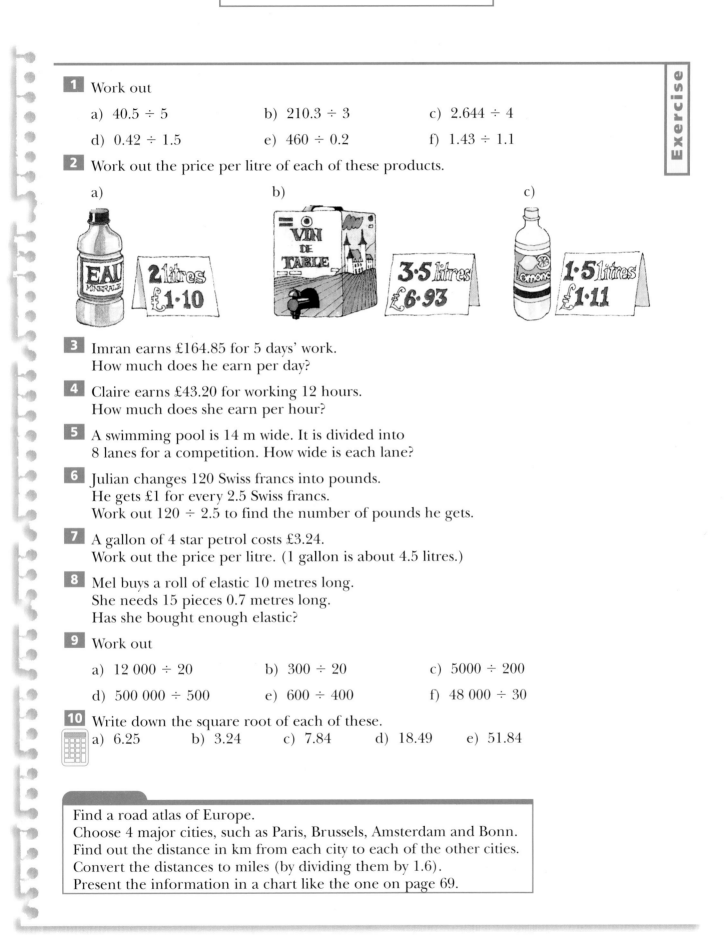

Exercise

1 Work out

a) $40.5 \div 5$ b) $210.3 \div 3$ c) $2.644 \div 4$

d) $0.42 \div 1.5$ e) $460 \div 0.2$ f) $1.43 \div 1.1$

2 Work out the price per litre of each of these products.

a)

EAU MINERALE — 2 litres £1·10

b)

VIN DE TABLE — 3·5 litres £6·93

c)

Lemon — 1·5 litres £1·11

3 Imran earns £164.85 for 5 days' work.
How much does he earn per day?

4 Claire earns £43.20 for working 12 hours.
How much does she earn per hour?

5 A swimming pool is 14 m wide. It is divided into
8 lanes for a competition. How wide is each lane?

6 Julian changes 120 Swiss francs into pounds.
He gets £1 for every 2.5 Swiss francs.
Work out $120 \div 2.5$ to find the number of pounds he gets.

7 A gallon of 4 star petrol costs £3.24.
Work out the price per litre. (1 gallon is about 4.5 litres.)

8 Mel buys a roll of elastic 10 metres long.
She needs 15 pieces 0.7 metres long.
Has she bought enough elastic?

9 Work out

a) $12\,000 \div 20$ b) $300 \div 20$ c) $5000 \div 200$

d) $500\,000 \div 500$ e) $600 \div 400$ f) $48\,000 \div 30$

10 Write down the square root of each of these.

a) 6.25 b) 3.24 c) 7.84 d) 18.49 e) 51.84

Find a road atlas of Europe.
Choose 4 major cities, such as Paris, Brussels, Amsterdam and Bonn.
Find out the distance in km from each city to each of the other cities.
Convert the distances to miles (by dividing them by 1.6).
Present the information in a chart like the one on page 69.

Finishing off

Now that you have finished this chapter you should be able to

★ write tenths and hundredths in decimal form

★ write decimals as tenths and hundredths

★ write a half, a quarter and three quarters in decimal form

★ add and subtract decimals

★ multiply decimals

★ divide decimals

★ work out squares and square roots

Use the questions in the next exercise to check that you understand everything.

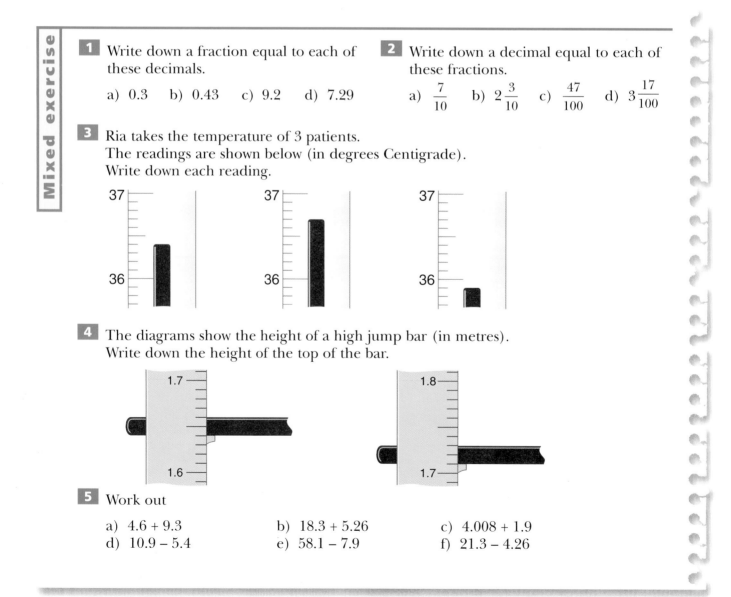

Mixed exercise

1 Write down a fraction equal to each of these decimals.

a) 0.3   b) 0.43   c) 9.2   d) 7.29

2 Write down a decimal equal to each of these fractions.

a) $\frac{7}{10}$ b) $2\frac{3}{10}$ c) $\frac{47}{100}$ d) $3\frac{17}{100}$

3 Ria takes the temperature of 3 patients.
The readings are shown below (in degrees Centigrade).
Write down each reading.

4 The diagrams show the height of a high jump bar (in metres).
Write down the height of the top of the bar.

5 Work out

a) 4.6 + 9.3
d) 10.9 − 5.4

b) 18.3 + 5.26
e) 58.1 − 7.9

c) 4.008 + 1.9
f) 21.3 − 4.26

6 Work out the amount each person spends at this snack bar.

a) Anna buys a can of cola and a jacket potato with beans.

b) Reena buys 2 cartons of apple juice, a vegeburger and a yoghurt.

c) Alex buys a bacon bap and a burger.

d) Kit buys 5 packs of biscuits.

e) Lu buys 3 cans and 2 cartons.

SNACK BAR MENU £
Cans (cola, orange) 0·52
Cartons (apple, orange) 0·40
Jacket potatoes
  (cheese or beans) 1·10
Burger in a bun 1·29
Vegeburger in a bun 1·09
Bacon bap 1·29
Yoghurt 0·32
Pack of biscuits 0·25

7 Work out

a) 7.1×100 b) 2.16×1000 c) 3.32×200 d) 0.04×40

8 An office desk is 180 cm wide. How many metres is this?

9 Barbara has £120 to change to dollars. She gets $1.65 for each £1.

How many dollars does she get altogether?

10 Wesley buys 0.6 kg of tomatoes and 1.2 kg of bananas at this stall.

a) How much does it cost?

b) How much change does he get from a £20 note?

Tomatoes £1.40 per kg

Bananas £0.95 per kg

11 Hannah fits a wash-basin in the middle of a bathroom wall. The basin is 44.6 cm wide, and the wall is 87 cm wide.

How much space is there at each side of the basin?

12 Work out

a) $42 \div 3.5$ b) $6 \div 0.25$ c) $25 \div 2.5$ d) $7.2 \div 1.5$

13 A videotape box is 2.5 cm thick.

How many can be stored on a shelf 80 cm long?

14 Find the value of

a) 7.2^2 b) $\sqrt{7.84}$

c) 4.9^2 d) $\sqrt{29.16}$

Find everyday objects (5 in all) with lengths as near as you can to 1 cm, 5 cm, 10 cm, 50 cm and 1 m.

Measure each of your objects and state its length.

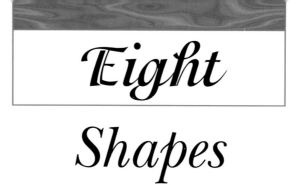

Eight

Shapes

Sorting shapes

Look at these shapes.

Can you organise them into groups? (There are lots of ways of doing this.)

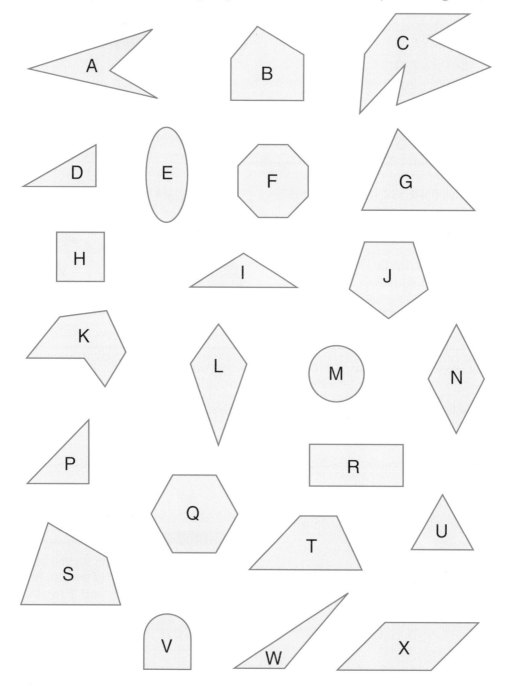

1 Here are some groups of shapes from the opposite page.

For each one, say what rule has been used to put shapes into the group.

You may know a special name for some of the groups.

a) D, G, I, P, U, W
b) A, H, L, N, R, S, T, X
c) B, J
d) K, Q
e) C, F
f) F, H, J, Q, U

2 There are many other ways of putting the shapes into groups.

For each of the groups described below, write down the letters for all the shapes which would fit in the group.

a) shapes with curves in them
b) shapes with at least one right angle
c) shapes with at least one obtuse angle
d) shapes with at least one reflex angle
e) shapes with at least one pair of parallel lines
f) shapes with all sides the same length

Remember:
a right angle is a 90° angle,
an acute angle is an angle less than 90°,
an obtuse angle is an angle between 90° and 180°,
a reflex angle is an angle bigger than 180°.

Look at these triangles. For each one, say how many sides are the same length, and what different types of angles it has (acute angles, right angles or obtuse angles).

A   B   C   D   J   E   H   G   F   I   K

Group each triangle with others that have the same description.

How many different types of triangle are there altogether?

Triangles

A shape with three sides is called a **triangle**.

Triangles can be described by how many sides with the same length they have.

A triangle whose three sides are all the same length is called an **equilateral triangle**.

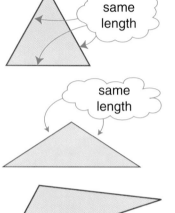

same length

A triangle that has two sides the same length and the third side a different length is called an **isosceles triangle**.

same length

A triangle whose sides are all of different lengths is called a **scalene triangle**.

Another way of describing triangles is by what sort of angles they have.

An **acute-angled triangle** has three acute angles (all its angles are less than 90°).

An acute-angled triangle can be equilateral, isosceles or scalene.

A **right-angled triangle** has one right angle (a 90° angle).

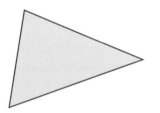

right angle

A right-angled triangle can be isosceles or scalene.

An **obtuse-angled triangle** has one obtuse angle (an angle greater than 90°).

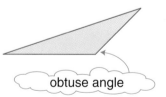

An obtuse-angled triangle can be isosceles or scalene.

obtuse angle

Why is it impossible to have a triangle which is right-angled and equilateral?

Why it is impossible to have a triangle which is obtuse-angled and equilateral?

Exercise

1 Which of these triangles is
   a) a right-angled scalene triangle?
   b) an obtuse-angled isosceles triangle?
   c) an equilateral triangle?
   d) an acute-angled scalene triangle?
   e) a right-angled isosceles triangle?
   f) an obtuse-angled scalene triangle?
   g) an acute-angled isosceles triangle?

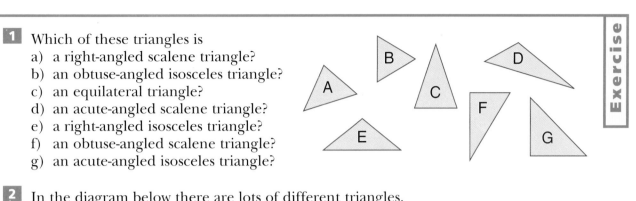

2 In the diagram below there are lots of different triangles.

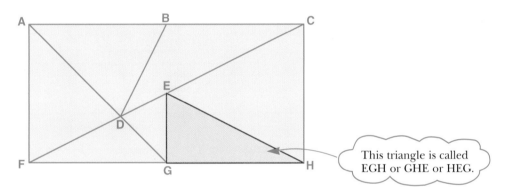

This triangle is called EGH or GHE or HEG.

Find as many different triangles as you can. Describe each triangle that you find.

Write down your answers like this:

EGH is a right-angled scalene triangle

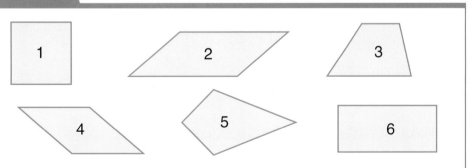

For each of these four-sided shapes, say which of the statements in the list below are true.

If you know the special name for the shape, write that down as well.

A Four equal sides   B Two pairs of equal sides
C No equal sides   D Four right angles
E Two pairs of equal angles   F One pair of equal angles
G Two pairs of parallel sides H One pair of parallel sides

Quadrilaterals

Any shape with four sides is called a **quadrilateral**.

Some quadrilaterals have special names.

A **square** has four equal sides. All of its angles are right angles.

A **rectangle** has two pairs of equal sides. All of its angles are right angles.

A **parallelogram** has its opposite sides equal and parallel.

A **rhombus** has four equal sides. Its opposite sides are parallel.

A **kite** has two pairs of equal sides. The equal sides are next to each other.

A **trapezium** has one pair of parallel sides.

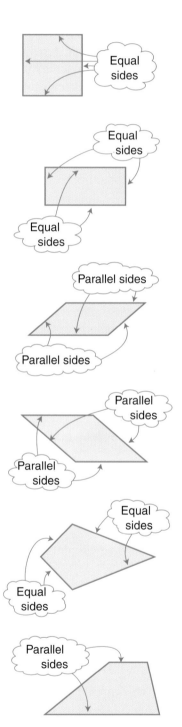

A shape with four sides which is none of these special shapes is called an **irregular quadrilateral**.

1 Draw each of these shapes.

For each one, show all of its lines of reflection symmetry.

   a) square   b) rectangle   c) rhombus

   d) parallelogram   e) kite   f) trapezium

2 Here is a quadrilateral on a 3×3 pinboard.

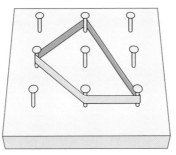

Find as many other different quadrilaterals as you can on a 3×3 pinboard.

Draw each one and write the name of the shape (e.g. parallelogram) beside your drawing.

3 Write 'T' (for true) or 'F' (for false) for each of these statements. In each case, explain your choice.

   a) A square is a special kind of rectangle.

   b) A rectangle is a special kind of square.

   c) A parallelogram is a special kind of rhombus.

   d) A rhombus is a special kind of parallelogram.

   e) A kite is a special kind of trapezium.

   f) A square is a special kind of trapezium.

What other statements like these can you find? Which ones are true?

Trace this right-angled triangle 4 times.

Cut your triangles out so that you have 4 identical triangles.

Put them together to make as many other shapes as you can. Draw each shape and (where possible) give its name.

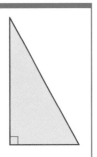

Other kinds of shapes

Polygons

Shapes with three or more straight sides are called **polygons**

You have already met two kinds of polygon: the triangle and the quadrilateral.

If all the sides of a polygon are the same length, and all its angles are the same, it is called a **regular polygon**.

Otherwise it is called an **irregular polygon**.

 What is the special name for a regular quadrilateral?

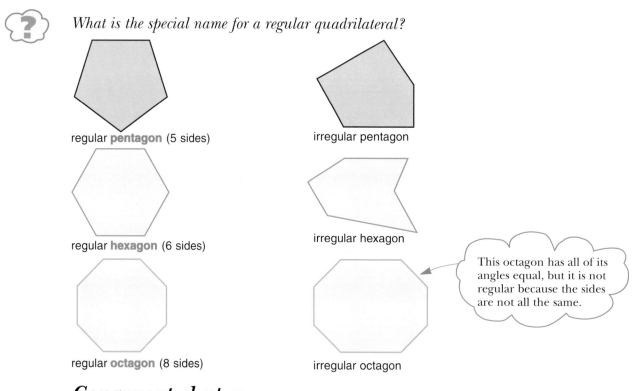

regular **pentagon** (5 sides)

irregular pentagon

regular **hexagon** (6 sides)

irregular hexagon

regular **octagon** (8 sides)

irregular octagon

This octagon has all of its angles equal, but it is not regular because the sides are not all the same.

Congruent shapes

Trace triangle A.

Try to fit your tracing over each of the other triangles. You may need to turn it over for some of them. Which triangles fit the tracing exactly?

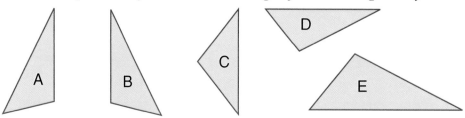

Shapes which are exactly the same shape and size are called **congruent**. Congruent shapes may be turned round or flipped over, but the tracing of a shape will always fit exactly over a shape which is congruent to it.

9   a)   Copy or trace the polygons below and draw on the lines of symmetry. Label each shape with its correct name.

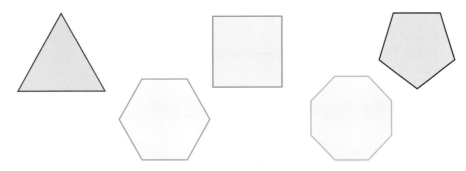

     b)   How many lines of symmetry do you think a regular polygon with 50 sides would have?

2   Which of these shapes are congruent to shape A?

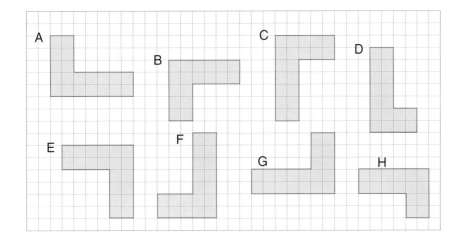

Investigations

1   Copy this pattern on to squared paper.

     How many patterns, congruent to this one, can you draw on a 3 × 3 grid?

2   Design your own pattern and draw some other patterns that are congruent to it.

What shapes are used to make the cover of a football?

How many of each shape are needed?

How big is each shape?

Circles

The circle is a very familiar shape.

We see circles all around us, wherever we go.

Car and bicycle wheels, dinner plates and CDs are all circles.

There are several different ways of measuring circles to find out how big they are.

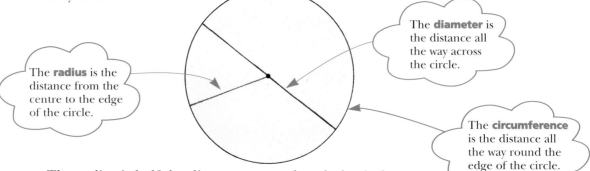

The **diameter** is the distance all the way across the circle.

The **radius** is the distance from the centre to the edge of the circle.

The **circumference** is the distance all the way round the edge of the circle.

The radius is half the distance across the whole circle.

So the radius is half the diameter.

The circumference is difficult to measure because it curves.

It is easier to measure if you use a piece of string.

The tip of a windscreen wiper traces out part of a circle.
Part of a circle is called an **arc**.

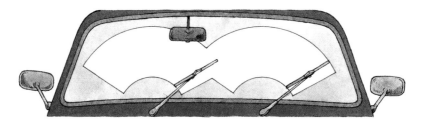

The bicycle wheel touches the line of the road. A line which just touches a circle is called a **tangent**.

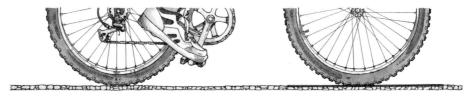

A line which goes across the circle from one point on the circumference to another is called a **chord**.

arc

chord

tangent

1 Give 5 examples of circles in everyday life.

(Choose ones that have not been mentioned on the left-hand page!)

2 Use compasses to draw

a) a circle with radius 4 cm
b) a circle with radius 5.4 cm
c) a circle with diameter 7 cm.
  (Hint: work out the radius of the circle first.)

3 Use a piece of string to measure roughly the circumference of each of the circles you drew in question 2.

Investigations

1 This is how to draw a pattern called a Mystic Rose.

1 Draw a circle. Mark 5 points, roughly equally spaced, on the circumference.

2 Draw chords from one point to each of the other points.

3 Now do the same for each of the other points. You can colour the pattern if you like.

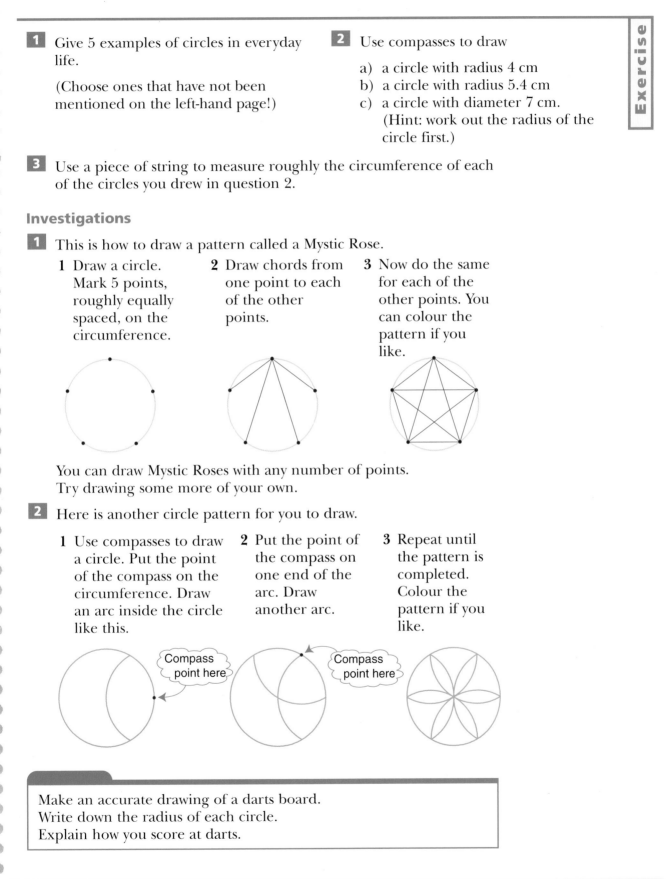

You can draw Mystic Roses with any number of points.
Try drawing some more of your own.

2 Here is another circle pattern for you to draw.

1 Use compasses to draw a circle. Put the point of the compass on the circumference. Draw an arc inside the circle like this.

2 Put the point of the compass on one end of the arc. Draw another arc.

3 Repeat until the pattern is completed. Colour the pattern if you like.

Compass point here

Compass point here

Make an accurate drawing of a darts board.
Write down the radius of each circle.
Explain how you score at darts.

Finishing off

Now that you have finished this chapter you should recognise

★ an equilateral triangle, an isosceles triangle and a scalene triangle

★ an acute-angled triangle, a right-angled triangle and an obtuse-angled triangle

★ a square, a rectangle, a parallelogram, a rhombus, a kite and a trapezium

★ a quadrilateral, a polygon, a pentagon, a hexagon and an octagon

★ the difference between a regular and an irregular shape

★ congruent shapes

★ a circumference, a radius, a diameter, a chord, an arc and a tangent of a circle

Use the questions in the next exercise to check that you understand everything.

Mixed exercise

Look back at the shapes on page 74 to answer questions 1 – 4.

1 Which of them are

a) triangles?   b) quadrilaterals?   c) pentagons?

d) hexagons?   e) octagons?   f) circles?

2 Which of the triangles are

a) isosceles?   b) scalene?

c) equilateral?   d) right-angled?

3 Which of the quadrilaterals are

a) rectangles?   b) parallelograms?

c) kites?   d) trapeziums ('trapezia')?

4 Which of the pentagons, hexagons and octagons are regular?

5 a) Sketch a circle as nearly as you can.

b) On your circle, draw and label a diameter, a radius, a chord and a tangent.

6 Look at Helen's design for a patchwork baby quilt. How many of each of these shapes does she need?

a) right-angled triangles b) squares

c) parallelograms d) trapezia e) isosceles triangles

What kind(s) of symmetry does the design have?

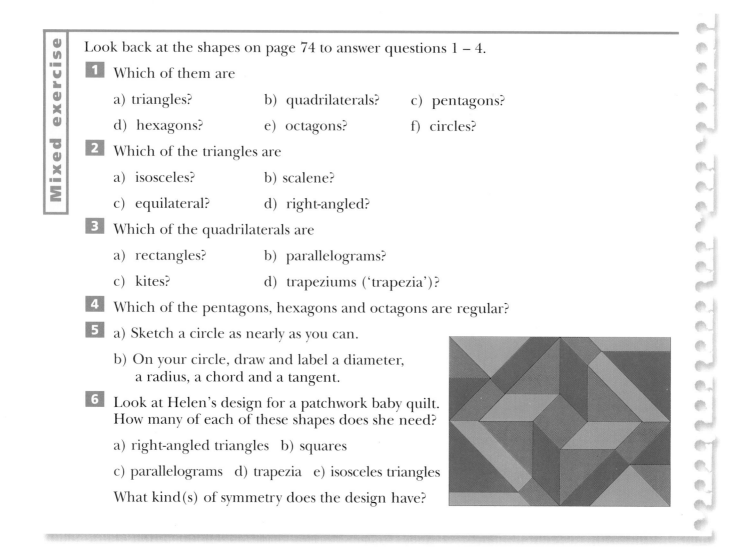

Investigation

a) Find as many triangles as you can on a 3 × 3 pinboard.

   Draw the triangles on squared paper.

   Here are two examples.

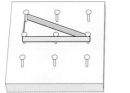 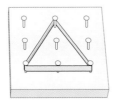

b) Describe each triangle that you have drawn.

   Use the words isosceles, scalene, right-angled, acute-angled and obtuse-angled.

c) Can you make an equilateral triangle?

Design a patchwork or mosaic of your own. Draw your design on squared paper.

Make a list of the shapes you have used.

What kind(s) of symmetry does your design have?

Collect 5 or 6 different-sized tins (such as baked beans tins, baby-milk tins, tomato purée tins and so on).

Tin	Circumference (cm)	Diameter (cm)	Circumference ÷ Diameter
Baked Beans			
Tomato Purée			

Make a table like this.

Use a piece of string to measure the circumference of each tin as accurately as you can.
Use a ruler or any other suitable method for measuring the diameter.
Write your results in the table.
Using a calculator, divide the circumference of each tin by its diameter.
Put the result in the last column.
When you have finished, look carefully at the figures in the last column.
Do you notice anything?
Write a sentence or two to explain your conclusions.

Nine

Percentages

25%, 50% and 75%

Student Survey findings

FACT **50% of Year 10 have part-time jobs**

The survey says that 50% of students have a part-time job.

That means 50 out of every 100.

You can show this in a 10 × 10 square like this:

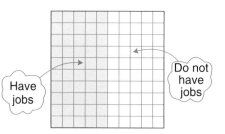

Have jobs

Do not have jobs

What fraction is shaded? Write the fraction in its simplest form.

Write this fraction as a decimal.

You can see that 50% is the same as $\frac{1}{2}$ or 0.5. So half of Year 10 students have part-time jobs.

FACT **25% of Year 10 cannot swim**

Again you can show this in a 10 × 10 square:

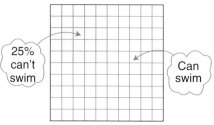

25% can't swim

Can swim

What fraction of the students can't swim? Write the fraction in its simplest form.

You can see that 25% is the same as $\frac{1}{4}$ or 0.25.

You can also see from the diagram that 75% of the students can swim.

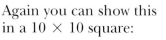

What fraction of the students can swim?

75% is the same as $\frac{3}{4}$ or 0.75.

1 Copy and complete this table.

Fraction	Decimal	Percentage
$\frac{1}{4}$		
	0.5	
		75%

For questions 2 to 6 choose A, B or C. Use this pie chart to answer questions 2, 3 and 4. It shows the results of Ann's survey of the customers at her fitness centre. She asked them how they first heard of the centre.

2 The percentage of customers who heard about it from friends is

A less than 25%   B 25%

C more than 25%

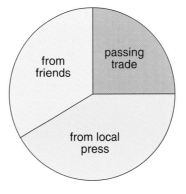

3 The percentage of customers who read about it in the local press is

A less than 50%   B 50%

C more than 50%

4 The percentage of customers who are 'passing trade' is

A less than 25%   B 25%

C more than 25%

5 Ben scores 11 marks out of 20 in a test. Is this

A less than 50%   B 50%   or   C more than 50%?

6 This is a small garden of flower beds and paving slabs.

Is the area covered by flower beds

A less than 50%   B 50%

or   C more than 50%?

You are asked to design a new flag for a small island.

It must be 50% blue and 50% green, and made of 4 rectangles as shown.

How many different flags are possible?

Finding percentages

Leo finds that 7 out of every 10 customers choose chicken.

What is this as a percentage?

You can draw this as 10 columns like this:

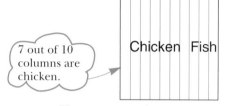

You can see that

7 out of 10 is the same as 70 out of 100, or 70%;

3 out of 10 is the same as 30 out of 100, or 30%.

Another way to do this is to use equivalent fractions:

$$\frac{7}{10} = \frac{70}{100} = 70\%, \qquad \frac{3}{10} = \frac{30}{100} = 30\%$$

Using equivalent fractions in the same way,

$$\frac{1}{10} = \frac{10}{100} = 10\%, \qquad \frac{1}{20} = \frac{5}{100} = 5\%$$

Example

Write   a) $\frac{9}{10}$ b) $\frac{2}{5}$ as percentages.

Solution

a) $\frac{9}{10} = \frac{90}{100} = 90\%$ b) $\frac{2}{5} = \frac{4}{10} = \frac{40}{100} = 40\%$

Example

In a maternity hospital 520 out of 1000 births are boys.

What percentage are   a) boys?   b) girls?

Solution

a)   520 out of 1000 is $\frac{520}{1000}$:

$$\frac{520}{1000} = \frac{52}{100} = 52\%$$

b)   The girls must be $100\% - 52\% = 48\%$.

You can change decimals into percentages without doing any calculations.

0.17 is 17 hundredths, or 17%.

0.06 is 6 hundredths, or 6%.

Percentages

1 Look at the diagram.

What percentage of the cost of making a pair of jeans is

a) labour?

b) overheads?

c) materials?

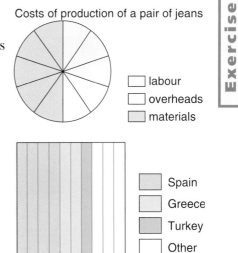

Costs of production of a pair of jeans

☐ labour
☐ overheads
☐ materials

2 Helen is a travel agent.

This diagram shows where her clients go on holiday.

a) What percentage go to Spain?

b) What percentage go to Greece?

c) What percentage go to Turkey?

☐ Spain
☐ Greece
☐ Turkey
☐ Other

3 Anna does an experiment on the air someone breathes out.

Here are her results in litres.

Total	Oxygen	Nitrogen	Carbon dioxide
200	32	160	8

a) What percentage is oxygen?

b) What percentage is nitrogen?

c) What percentage is carbon dioxide?

4 Here are three floor designs.

Border

Octo

Tapestry

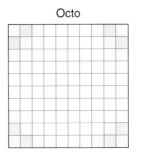

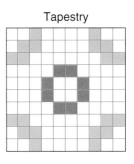

Each is made up of 100 square tiles.

a) What percentage of each floor is coloured?

b) Write each percentage as a fraction in its simplest form.

c) Write each percentage as a decimal.

Find a newspaper article and count the number of letters in each of the first 50 words.

What percentage of the words have 1 letter, 2 letters, 3 letters,…?

Show your results in a table.

Percentage calculations

70% Success rate

A catering firm takes on 300 trainees. 70% of them are successful, completing their training and getting qualifications.

How many trainees is this?

The number who are successful is 70% of 300.

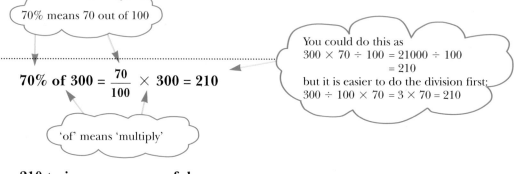

70% means 70 out of 100

You could do this as
$300 \times 70 \div 100 = 21000 \div 100$
$= 210$
but it is easier to do the division first:
$300 \div 100 \times 70 = 3 \times 70 = 210$

$$70\% \text{ of } 300 = \frac{70}{100} \times 300 = 210$$

'of' means 'multiply'

210 trainees are successful.

What percentage of the trainees are not successful?

How many trainees are not successful?

4% pay rise

Hasna earns £150 a week. She is given a 4% pay rise.

The pay rise is 4% of £150.

$$4\% \text{ of } 150 = \frac{4}{100} \times 150 = 6$$

How much is the pay rise?

How much does Hasna earn after the pay rise?

Carly buys this jacket.
The reduction is 40% of £70.

$$40\% \text{ of } 70 = \frac{40}{100} \times 70 = 28$$

How much is the reduction?

How much does Carly pay for the jacket?

1 Work out

a) 75% of 400

b) 20% of 600

c) 40% of 350

d) 50% of 144

e) 8% of 125

f) 60% of 225

g) 2% of 100

h) 1% of 200

i) 15% of 400

j) 10% of 220

k) 5% of 2000

l) 20% of 80

2 Claire earns £9000 a year. She is given a pay rise of 10%.

How much extra money does she get?

3 What are the savings on each of these cars when you buy in June?

4 6% of the cups made at a pottery are faulty.

How many faulty cups would you expect in a batch of 400?

5 Sam's heating bills are £800 a year.

She insulates her loft and so her heating bills fall by 20%.

How much does she save each year?

6 Rebecca gets 10% off a holiday priced at £400.

How much does she pay?

7 Shamil's railway season ticket cost £200 last year.

The price has gone up by 6%.

How much does it cost this year?

8 James receives a bill for £250.

He gets a 2% discount by paying within a week.

How much does he pay?

Get a copy of the Passenger's Charter from one of the railway companies.

Look through it and find the percentage refunds you can get if the trains run late.

Say exactly when you can get a refund.

Finishing off

> ## Now that you have finished this chapter you should
>
> ★ know the fraction and decimal equivalents of 25%, 50% and 75%
>
> ★ be able to change a percentage to a fraction or a decimal
>
> ★ be able to calculate a percentage of a number
>
> ★ be able to calculate the outcome of a percentage increase or decrease

Use the questions in the next exercise to check that you understand everything.

Mixed exercise

1 Work out

a) 10% of £750

b) 50% of £25

c) 40% of 400

d) 26% of 2000

e) 30% of 40

f) 50% of £4.50

g) 50% of £50 000

h) 75% of 16

i) 8% of 25

2 Copy and complete this table.

Fraction	Decimal	Percentage
1/10		
	0·2	
		25%
7/10		
	0·8	
		90%

3 Pat's food intake is 28% fat, 15% protein and the rest is carbohydrates.

What percentage is carbohydrates?

4 What percentage of these fish are

a) angel fish (yellow)?
b) goldfish (orange)?
c) starfish (red)?

What percentage of the fish are

d) not angel fish?
e) not goldfish?
f) not starfish?

5 Ben usually buys a 250 ml can of orange at lunchtime.

One day the can is larger and is marked '20% extra'.

How much orange does this larger can contain?

6 Crystal buys chocolates priced at £800 for her shop.

She gets a 15% trade discount.

How much does she pay?

7 Jordan is doing a survey by post.

He sends out 250 questionnaires and expects to get 30% back.

How many replies does he expect?

8 Sally wants to buy a washing machine.

She sees the model she wants in two different stores.

a) Which store offers the best deal if she wants it delivered?

b) Which store offers the best deal if she does not want it delivered?

Investigations

1

How many different ways are there of colouring 50% of this figure red and the rest white? (You may not colour part squares).

2

How many different ways are there of colouring 40% of this figure blue and the remainder white? (You may not colour part squares).

Choose 5 kinds of packaged food.

On each one, find the label that tells you the amount of fat, protein and carbohydrate per 100 g.

Write the amounts as percentages in a table.

Ten

Statistics

Recording data

Karen's department at work decide to have an evening out together. They ask Karen to organise it.

Karen goes round asking everyone what they would most like to do.

She records their answers like this:

This is called a **tally chart**.

This means 5.

Disco   ⊬⊬

Greyhound racing   IIII

Ten-pin bowling   ⊬⊬ III

Ice-skating   II

Pub   I

Ten-pin bowling has the most tallies. It has 5 + 3 = 8. It is the most popular.

These are the tallies.

Keeping a tally is an easy way to count things. It is easy to add them up afterwards too, especially if you can count in fives.

When numbers are collected like this they are called **data**.

After she has collected the data, Karen shows the results to everyone as a **frequency table**.

Activity	Disco	Greyhounds	Bowling	Skating	Pub
Frequency	5	4	8	2	1

These are the frequencies.

When you add these frequencies up you get 20. This is the number of people who are going out for the evening.

In this case the data are **categorical** because they are grouped by categories such as *ice-skating* and *disco*.

If the data are grouped by numbers, for example, the ages of a class of students, they are called **numerical**.

1 The evening is to end with a meal, so Karen also asks everyone where they would like to eat.

Here is her tally chart.

Fish + chips |

Indian   ++++ ++++ |

Chinese ||

Pub meal ++++ |

a) Show their answers as a frequency table.

b) Which was the most popular choice?

c) Has Karen asked everyone? Explain your answer.

2 Samantha goes to a theme park with a party of friends. Afterwards she asks them which ride they liked best. Here are their answers.

Dragon's tail   ++++ ++++ ||

Splashdown   ++++ ||

Pirate Plank   ++++ |||

Octopus |||

a) Show their answers as a frequency table.

b) How many are in the party?

c) Which is the most popular ride?

Find out the most popular music group among your friends or classmates.

Design a tally chart and use it to record their answers when you question them.

Show the results both as tallies and as a frequency table.

Displaying data

People often show their data in pictures. There are many ways of doing this. Some of these are shown here and others later in this chapter.

Pictograms

This pictogram shows Karen's data about what people want to do for their evening out.

All the pictures on a pictogram must be the same size.

This means one person.

Disco

Greyhounds

Bowling

Skating

Pub

😊 = 2 people

Bar charts

Bar charts can be drawn vertically like the one below, or horizontally.

Notice that

- all the bars have the same thickness;

- the gaps between the bars are all the same;

- each bar is labelled in the middle.

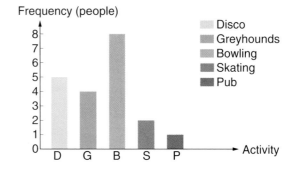

Frequency (people)

Disco
Greyhounds
Bowling
Skating
Pub

D G B S P   Activity

Which do you prefer, the pictogram or the bar chart? They both show the same data.

Vertical line charts

A vertical line chart is often used for showing numerical data. This vertical line chart shows the number of children living in the 40 houses on one street.

It is like a bar chart with very thin bars.

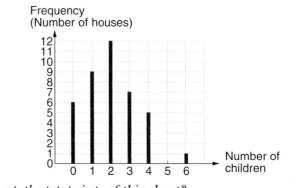

Frequency
(Number of houses)

0 1 2 3 4 5 6   Number of children

Why is it misleading to join up the top points of this chart?

1 One day in January, a jogging club asks all its members how many days they have been out running during the last week.

Here are their answers.

0	3	7	0	0	1	2	1	0	3
1	2	2	1	0	1	3	4	1	2
2	3	1	1	1	4	7	7	1	2

a) Record these figures on a tally chart.

b) Record the figures on a frequency table.

c) How many members does the club have?

d) Draw a vertical line chart to show the data.

The vertical line chart below shows the results when the members are asked the same question in June.

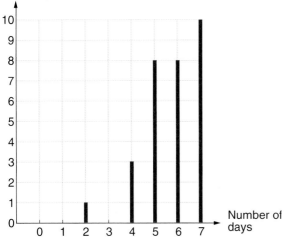

Frequency (people)

Number of days

e) Look at the two vertical line charts, yours and the one above.

What difference do you notice?

Give a possible explanation for the difference.

2 A book on pets includes this pictogram showing the results of a survey into what happens when dogs meet other dogs.

Play	🐶 🐶 🐶
Friendly sniff	🐶 🐶 🐶 🐶 🐶
No reaction	🐶 🐶 🐶
Growl	🐶 🐶
Fight	🐶

🐶 = 2 dogs

a) Make a frequency table showing how many dogs there are in each category.

b) What is the total number of dogs?

c) What percentage of dogs growl or fight?

d) Do you think these are good categories?

e) Draw a bar chart to illustrate these data.

Look through newspapers and magazines and find at least 2 examples of pictograms and 2 examples of bar charts or vertical line charts. Cut them out and paste them on a piece of paper.

Pie charts

Here is part of a report on an airline's business.

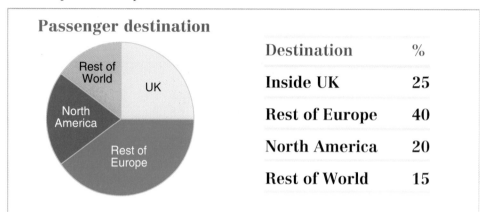

Passenger destination

Destination	%
Inside UK	25
Rest of Europe	40
North America	20
Rest of World	15

You can show this information on a pie chart.

It has a number of sectors. In the chart below, each sector is a different colour.

To draw a pie chart you need the angle for each sector.

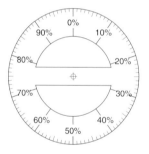

In this example an easy way is to use an angle measurer that is marked in percentages (sometimes called a pie chart scale).

But you should also know how to work out the angles in degrees, as follows.

The whole circle is 360°, so you work out the sector angles like this:

Inside UK $\frac{25}{100} \times 360° = 90°$

Rest of Europe $\frac{40}{100} \times 360° = 144°$

North America $\frac{20}{100} \times 360° = ...$

Rest of the World $\frac{15}{100} \times 360° = ...$

> Work out these two angles yourself to check that you can get the right answers.

Add up all the angles and check that they come to 360°.

Once you know the angles, you use a protractor or angle measurer to draw them.

1 In an election 40% of people vote for the Social Democrats, 30% for the Liberal Alliance, 20% for the Christian Democrats and the rest don't vote. You are going to show this on a pie chart.

   a) What percentage don't vote?
   b) Show that the angle for Social Democrats is 144°.
   c) Find the angles of the sectors for the other parties, and for those who don't vote.
   d) Draw the pie chart.

2 In this question you are going to draw a pie chart for Karen's data from page 94.

Activity	Disco	Greyhounds	Bowling	Skating	Pub
Frequency	5	4	8	2	1

There are 20 people in the party so each person has 360° ÷ 20 = 18°.

   a) Show that the disco sector has an angle of 90°.
   b) Find the angles for the other activities.
   c) Draw the pie chart.

3 This pie chart illustrates the results of a football team's matches one season.

The team played 60 matches.

   a) How many degrees is 1 match?
   b) Show that they lost 20 matches.
   c) How many matches did they win?
   d) How many matches did they draw?
   e) They score 3 points for a win, 1 for a draw and 0 for a loss.
      How many points did they get in the season?

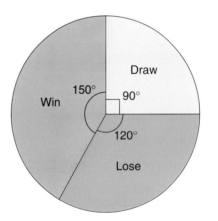

In the game of Shove-penny a coin is pushed along a board like this to score points.

Use a large sheet of paper to make a board and play the game 30 times.

Draw a pie chart to illustrate your results.

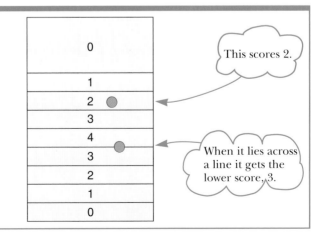

Grouping data

Sometimes it is easier to look at data when they are grouped. The figures below are the number of penalty points that some drivers have on their licences 2 years after passing their tests.

| 0 3 3 0 0 | 4 4 0 0 0 | 0 3 3 0 0 |
| 1 0 5 3 0 0 | 3 0 4 0 0 | 1 1 0 3 0 4 |

It is easier to see these as a grouped frequency table

Penalty points	0–2	3–5	6–8	9–11
Drivers (frequency)	16	12	0	2

Most people do not have many penalty points, if any, but two are near the limit of 12. If they reach 12 during the next year they will be banned from driving.

The number of points you get is always a whole number. You cannot get $4\frac{1}{2}$ or 5.8 points.

In ten-pin bowling you can knock over 9 skittles or 10 skittles but not $9\frac{1}{2}$ skittles.

These are examples of **discrete** data: you can't have 'in-between' values.

Some data can have 'in-between' values, for example people's heights in centimetres. These data are called **continuous**.

Before you can draw a diagram to show continuous data you must put them into groups.

The figures below are the heights in cm of the members of a youth club.

| 152.1 | 150.0 | 160.3 | 140.7 | 128.0 | 134.1 | 135.7 | 151.5 | 163.4 | 181.0 |
| 182.8 | 180.8 | 154.6 | 161.5 | 171.4 | 129.2 | 151.8 | 138.4 | 153.4 | 165.0 |

These can be put into groups, for example, from 120 cm up to 130 cm, from 130 cm up to 140 cm, and so on.

These data can be shown in a frequency chart.

Notice that

- there are no gaps between the bars;

- all the bars have the same thickness;

- the heights are written at the left and right edges of the bars, not in the middle.

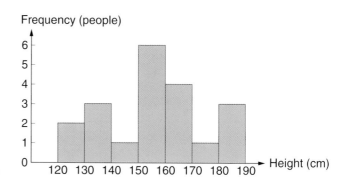

1 Arif wants to know if more babies are born at some times of the year than others.

He asks 24 people what month they were born in.

June	Feb	Jan	July	Dec	May	Sept	June	Nov	May
Oct	Jan	Sept	Aug	June	Oct	Aug	Nov	April	Feb
Aug	Sept	June	Sept						

Arif groups the data by season.

a) Copy and complete this frequency table.

Season	Winter Dec, Jan, Feb	Spring March, April, May	Summer June, July, Aug	Autumn Sept, Oct, Nov
Frequency (people)				

b) Draw a bar chart to illustrate the frequency table.

c) Do you think Arif has collected enough data to draw any conclusions?

2 The committee of a squash and tennis club are worried that not enough young people are coming to play.

They record the ages of people who come the next day.

76	69	68	70	12	15	16	18	19	41
36	27	49	56	61	45	39	33	26	44
52	53	36	24	31	41	43	44	42	19
18	18	42	53	21					

a) Make a tally chart, using groups 10–19, 20–29, …
b) Make a frequency table.
c) Do you think there should be more young people playing?

> Notice that age 19 goes from your 19th birthday to the day before your 20th birthday.

3 A time trial for 30 students running 100 m is carried out.

Times are in seconds.

14.3	15.2	16.4	14.8	13.9	14.7	15.0	14.8	13.9	12.7
16.7	12.8	18.3	15.5	15.7	16.9	14.2	14.0	18.5	14.6
15.4	16.4	17.5	18.5	12.1	13.8	15.2	16.7	16.5	16.9

a) Make a tally chart, using groups 12.0–12.9, 13.0–13.9, …
b) Make a frequency table.
c) Draw a frequency chart.
d) Do you think the times are fast or slow?

Give a possible explanation for them being so.

> Keep a record of how long it takes you to get to school or college on 20 occasions.
> Show this on a frequency chart and explain its main features.

Other data displays

Line graphs

Nat is in hospital. Every 3 hours his temperature is taken and the points are plotted on a graph.

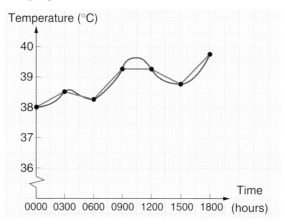

In the graph the points have been joined by the blue straight lines. This is usual on a line graph, but be careful: it can be misleading.

You don't know what happened between the points: it could have been the red curve.

When data are collected at time intervals, it is quite usual to show them on a graph like this.

Scatter diagrams

You will often collect data which involve 2 measurements.

In that case it is common to use a scatter diagram.

This scatter diagram shows the heights and weights of a group of women.

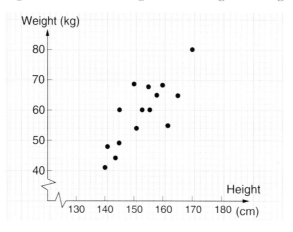

 What does this scatter diagram tell you?

1 Jake was born in January weighing 2.1 kg.

This is rather light for a baby so he was weighed every week for the next 10 weeks as a check.

Week	0	1	2	3	4	5	6	7	8	9	10
Weight	2.1	2.1	2.2	2.3	2.4	2.5	2.3	2.6	2.8	3.0	3.2

a) Plot these figures as a line graph.

b) Jake was ill one week.

Which week do you think it was?

c) Estimate Jake's weight at $9\frac{1}{2}$ weeks.

2 A group of male college students were weighed and then timed running 100 m.

The results are shown on this scatter diagram.

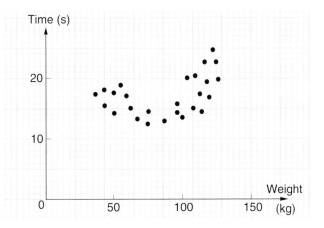

a) How many students were involved?

b) Describe what the scatter diagram tells you.

1 Run a distance of 200 metres as fast as you can.

Ask a friend to take your pulse rate every 2 minutes starting as soon as you stop running.

Show the results as a line graph.

How long does it take your pulse to return to normal?

Is this the same for other people?

2 Record the pulse rate of each student in your group before they take any exercise and immediately after running 200 metres.

Show the results on a scatter diagram.

Averages and spread

Natasha and Paul are part of a group that go ten-pin bowling.

They decide to arrive early so that they can have some practice shots.

These are their scores.

Natasha	7	7	5	4	7
Paul	10	10	3	1	

Who has done better?

Natasha's total score of 30 is greater than Paul's 24 but she had more turns.

You need to take an average. Here are three ways of doing it.

The **mode** is the most common score.

Natasha's mode is 7. What is Paul's mode?

The **mean** is the total divided by the number of turns played.

Natasha: 30 ÷ 5 = 6   Paul: 24 ÷ 4 = 6

They both have the same mean score.

The **median** is the middle score when the scores are put in order.

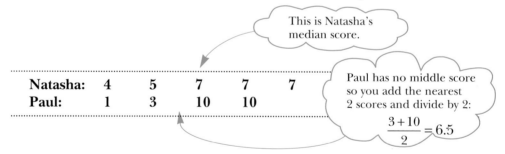

This is Natasha's median score.

Natasha: 4   5   7   7   7
Paul: 1   3   10   10

Paul has no middle score so you add the nearest 2 scores and divide by 2:
$$\frac{3+10}{2}=6.5$$

Natasha's median score of 7 is higher than Paul's 6.5.

Who has done the better? It depends which calculation you do.

Which calculation would Natasha want to use?

Which calculation would Paul want to use?

The **range** is the difference between the highest score and the lowest score.

Natasha: 7 − 4 = 3   Paul: 10 − 1 = 9

Paul has a larger range; his scores are more spread out.

Natasha has a smaller range: her scores are more consistent.

Exercise

1 Find the mean, median and mode of

  a) 1 1 2 3 8   b) 10 10 20 30 80

  c) 11 11 12 13 18   d) 101 101 102 103 108

2 Mr Doni is planning to start a company offering boat trips round the bay.

To find out what size of boats will be best he does 10 trial trips for one day. The numbers of people in them are

3   3   9   2   6   6   4   5   6   5

  a) Work out the mean, median and mode of these figures.

  b) Mr Doni has an 8-seater boat. How often will it be full?

3 In a survey on TV-watching, a group of boys record how many hours TV they watch each week.

Boys: 16   23   21   5   12   0   5   13   14   11

  a) Find the mean, median, mode and range of these figures.

A group of girls now do the same.

Girls: 9   11   4   16   15

  b) From these results do the boys or the girls watch more TV?

4 A hockey coach measures the times it takes members of the team to run 100 m (in seconds).

Hockey team: 15 14 12 11 13   14 11 13 12 11   15 11 13 14 16

  a) Calculate the mean, median, mode and range.

The coach then asks the PE staff to run 100 m.

PE staff: 11   18   11   12   13

  b) From these results, which group is the faster?

5 The pay of 12 employees in a small company is:

  £8 000   £8 000   £8 000   £8 000   £8 000

  £11 000   £11 000   £11 000   £13 000   £18 000

  £19 000   £65 000

  a) Find the mean, median, mode and range.

  b) What do you think the managing director earns?

Explain how batting and bowling averages are worked out for cricket. Give examples, using real players.

Finishing off

Now that you have finished this chapter you should be able to

★ make and use tally charts

★ construct a frequency table

★ draw pictograms, bar charts, vertical line charts, pie charts, frequency charts, line graphs and scatter diagrams

★ calculate the mean, median and mode of a set of data

★ calculate the range of a set of data

Use the questions in the next exercise to check that you understand everything.

Mixed exercise

1 The pictogram shows the holiday destinations for Monday's customers at a travel agency.

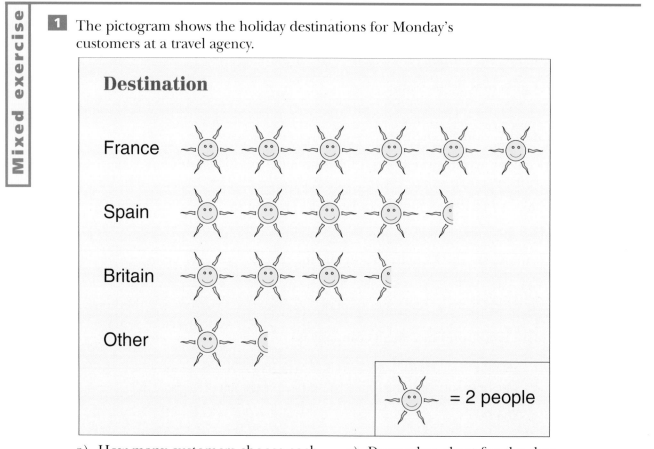

Destination

France

Spain

Britain

Other

= 2 people

a) How many customers choose each destination? Make a frequency table.

b) How many customers are represented in the pictogram?

c) Draw a bar chart for the data.

2 The pie chart below shows the mixture of cement, sand and coarse aggregate used in concrete for paths.

a) Measure the angles of the 3 sectors of the pie chart.

b) Write down the fraction of the concrete that is cement, the fraction that is sand and the fraction that is coarse aggregate.

c) Rachel's path will need 3 m^3 of concrete. How much cement, sand and coarse aggregate will she need?

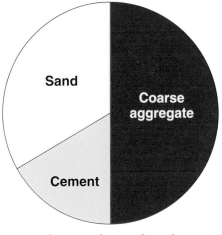

3 Here are the numbers of goals scored by a football team in their matches this year.

6   0   1   0   4   5   5   1   2   0

a) Find the mean, median, mode and range of these data.
b) What can you say about their performance?

Choose a suitable place beside a road and record the numbers of passengers in the first 50 cars that go by. (You will find it easier if there are two of you, one to call out the numbers and one to write them down.)

Now write a short report. Include diagrams to show your data.

4 A garden pond contains goldfish.

On 1 March each year the fish are counted.

Date (1 March)	1995	1996	1997	1998	1999	2000
Number of goldfish	12	16	17	20	10	18

a) Draw a graph to illustrate these data.

Use the horizontal axis for the date.

b) Can you answer the question 'How many goldfish were there on 1 September 1997?'?

5 Here are the weights, in kg, of 20 male students, all aged 18.

61 98 72 84 63   77 77 81 85 72

90 83 76 82 77   81 80 83 75 68

a) Use a tally chart like the one below to group the data.

Weight w (kg)	Tally
60 to 64	
65 to 69	
70 to 74	
75 to 79	
80 to 84	
85 to 89	
90 to 94	
95 to 99	

b) Make a frequency table.

c) A healthy weight for a male 18-year-old is about 70–80 kg.

Comment on the weights of this group of students.

Eleven

Directed numbers

Negative numbers

Peter has £40 in his bank account.

He has these bills to pay.

Gas Bill

£40.00

Car Repairs

£50.00

 How much is left in his account if he pays the gas bill?

How much is left if he then pays the car repairs bill?

He decides to pay both bills as he has a credit arrangement with the bank.

They allow him to owe them up to £100.

When he has paid the bills he is *overdrawn* by £50.

His balance is –£50.

This will be shown on his bank statement as £50.00 DR.

 Peter pays another bill, this time for £30.

What does his statement say now?

Here is the control panel for the lift in a large store.

Jo gets into the lift at the floor –1 and presses the button for floor 3.

How many floors does she go up?

You can see in the diagram that she goes up 4 floors.

She comes back to the lift at floor 3.

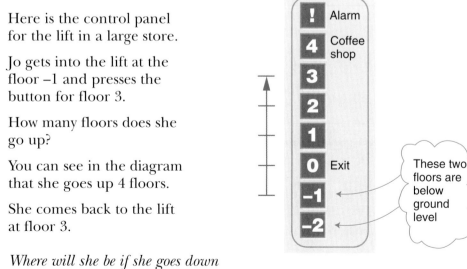

These two floors are below ground level

 Where will she be if she goes down

a) 2 floors?   *b) 3 floors?*   *c) 5 floors?*

What other situations can you think of in which negative numbers are used?

1 Look at the lift buttons opposite.

For each of these trips say how many floors the lift goes up or down.

Example: 1 to 3 is up 2 floors.

a) 3 to 4   b) 4 to 3   c) 3 to 0
d) 0 to –2   e) –2 to 2   f) 2 to –1

2 You have £200 in your bank account.

a) You pay a gas bill of £100. How much is left?

b) Now you pay £200 towards your holiday. How much is left?

c) You pay in your wages of £100. How much is in the account now?

3 Kate buys some jackets to sell on her market stall. They cost her £50 each.

a) She prices the jackets at £70.

What is the profit on a jacket?

b) To sell the last jacket she reduces its price to £45.

What is her profit on this one?

4

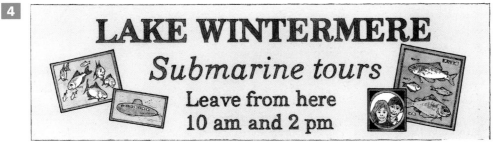

The diagram below shows the cross-section of the lake.

Work out how much the submarine goes up or down between

a) the start and the wreck
b) the wreck and the fish shoal
c) the fish shoal and the underwater cave
d) the underwater cave and the end.

Look at a bank statement that goes overdrawn.

Explain the entries in the 'balance' column.

Adding and subtracting

In winter, the temperature is often near zero.

It sometimes goes below zero.

The temperature one day is 2 °C.
At nightfall it drops by 5 °C.

The new temperature is

$$2 \text{ °C} - 5 \text{ °C} = -3 \text{ °C}$$

You can see this on the thermometer.

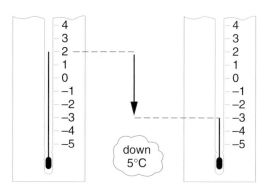

During the night, the temperature drops by another 1 °C.

The new temperature is

$$-3 \text{ °C} - 1 \text{ °C} = -4 \text{ °C}$$

Check this on the thermometer.

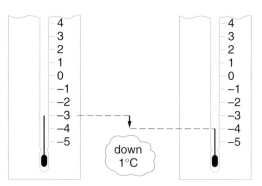

The next morning, the temperature rises by 7 °C.

The new temperature is

$$-4 \text{ °C} + 7 \text{ °C} = 3 \text{ °C}$$

Again you can check this on the thermometer.

 Which is warmer, 2 °C or –5 °C ?

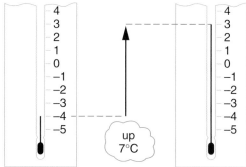

Drawing a number line helps you to add and subtract positive and negative numbers.

The scale on the thermometer is a number line.

Usually we draw number lines across the page, like this:

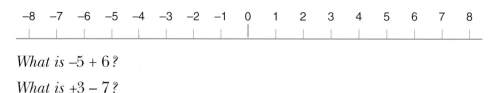

What is –5 + 6 ?

What is +3 – 7 ?

How would you draw a number line to help you work out +10 – 25 ?

1 Use the number line opposite to work out

    a) $5 - 1$ b) $0 - 4$ c) $1 - 7$ d) $-1 + 2$

    e) $5 + 2$ f) $-5 - 2$ g) $8 - 5$ h) $-8 + 5$

    i) $5 - 2$ j) $-5 + 2$ k) $3 + 4$ l) $-3 - 4$

2 Work out

    a) $20 - 21$ b) $-1 + 101$ c) $-50 + 30$ d) $1000 - 2000$

3 Copy and complete this table, using the information below.

The temperature in London is 4 °C.

Manchester is 5 °C colder than London.

Leeds is 2 °C colder than Manchester.

Inverness is 3 °C colder than Leeds.

Accra is 36 °C hotter than Inverness.

City	Temperature (°C)
London	
Manchester	
Leeds	
Inverness	
Accra	

4 This scale measures the water level of a river (in feet).

'Normal' river level is zero on the scale.

On Monday evening after a long spell of dry weather, there is a heavy rainstorm. This table shows the water level at 3-hourly intervals on Tuesday.

Mid-night	3 am	6 am	9 am	Noon	3 pm	6 pm	9 pm	Mid-night
–2	–1.5	–1	0	1	1.5	1	0	–1

a) What is the level at midnight on Monday?

b) How much has the river level risen by 3 am on Tuesday?

c) How much further has it risen by 3 pm?

d) How much does the level drop from 3 pm to 9 pm on Tuesday?

You have offered to make a special lunch for your family.

You are to serve it at 1 pm.

Choose the menu.

Write down all the stages in its preparation.

Work out how long before 1 pm each job has to be done.

Write a timetable for the morning to ensure that lunch is ready at exactly 1 pm.

Finishing off

Now that you have finished this chapter you should

- ★ know when to add and when to subtract
- ★ be able to add and subtract positive and negative numbers
- ★ be able to draw a number line with positive and negative numbers

Use the questions in the next exercise to check that you understand everything.

Mixed exercise

1 Work out

a) $6 - 8$ b) $-4 + 3$ c) $5 - 8$ d) $-2 + 7$

e) $-5 - 3$ f) $-10 + 6$ g) $20 - 25$ h) $-15 - 9$

2 Work out

a) £23.50 – £26.50   b) £4.25 – £5.00   c) £10.25 – £11.50

3 Which of these temperatures is colder:

a) $-2\ °C$ or $3\ °C$?   b) $0\ °C$ or $-1\ °C$?   c) $-2\ °C$ or $-4\ °C$?

4 Oliver has £125 in his bank account.

He writes a cheque for £58 to pay his phone bill.

Then he writes a cheque for £104 to pay for car repairs.

Finally he pays in a cheque for £29.

What is the new balance of his account?

5 When she is born, Rebecca weighs 4 kg.

The graph shows her weight gain after each of the next 3 weeks.

a) What does she weigh after 1 week?

b) What does she weigh after 2 weeks?

c) How much weight does she put on during the third week?

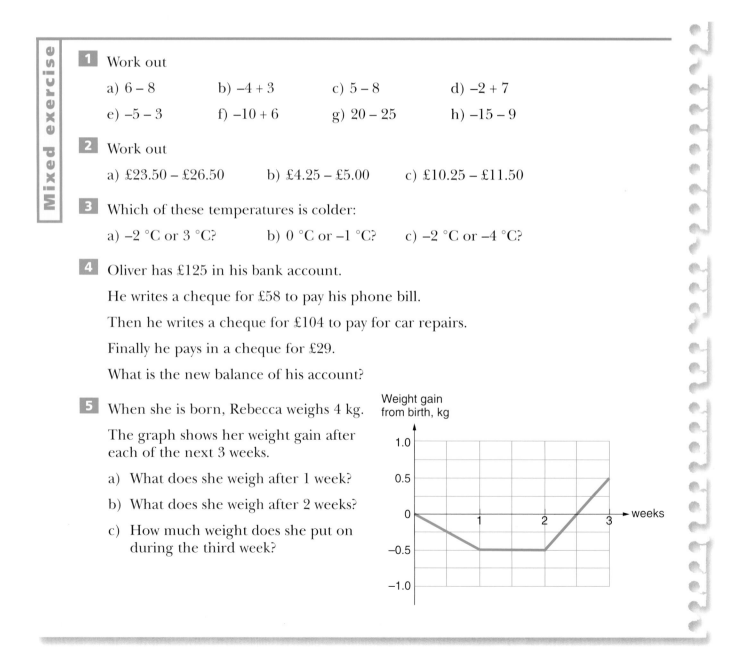

Weight gain from birth, kg

6 Local time in Calais is 1 hour ahead of local time in Dover.

The ferry crossing from one to the other takes 90 minutes.

a) A ferry leaves Dover at 0945 local time.

What will be the time in Calais when it arrives?

b) A ferry leaves Calais at 1635 local time.

What will be the time in Dover when it arrives?

7 Kim and Tessa plan to start a computer games company. They have saved £20,000 to start the company.

They will need to do a lot of work designing the games before they can start to sell them.

They go to the bank with this plan. It shows what they expect their bank balance to be each year.

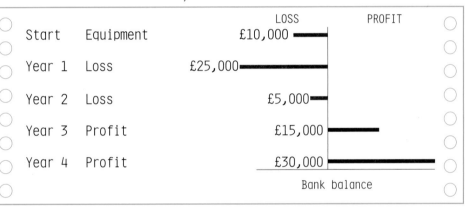

		LOSS	PROFIT
Start	Equipment	£10,000	
Year 1	Loss	£25,000	
Year 2	Loss	£5,000	
Year 3	Profit	£15,000	
Year 4	Profit	£30,000	

Bank balance

How much profit or loss do they expect to make in

a) Year 1?   b) Year 2?   c) Year 3?   d) Year 4?

Look at the people in your maths group.

Choose one person whose height you think is about average for the group.

Stick a piece of masking tape vertically on a wall.

Mark Mr (or Ms) Average's height on the tape.

Draw centimetre scales on the tape above (+) and below (−).

Now measure and record everyone else's height using your scales.

When you have finished, add up all the results.

Do you think your Mr (or Ms) Average really is close to the average height?

Twelve

Surveys

Planning a survey

Yvette is a keen swimmer.

One morning she gets this letter.

It is from her swimming club.

> AVONFORD SWIMMING CLUB
>
> Dear Yvette
>
> The club committee met last night to discuss how to attract new members.
>
> As a first step we would like a survey done in your school. Could you carry it out for us?

Step 1

Choose a topic that you find interesting.

Yvette agrees to do the survey.

She makes some notes.

> My swimming club wants me to find out whether people like swimming and if they are good at it.
> THINGS TO DO
> Write some questions to ask people
> Try them out on friends
> Get 60 copies made
> Get to school early + give to first 30 girls + 30 boys
> Make data collection sheet
> Write a report

Step 2

Write down why you are doing the survey and what you want to find out, and plan how to do the survey.

Yvette writes these questions.

> SWIMMING QUESTIONS
> 1 Can you swim?
> 2 Why do you like swimming?
> 3 How long do you take to do 1 length?
> 4 What stroke do you like best?

Step 3

Write the questions for your survey.

Yvette tries the questions out on some of her friends. Here are some of their answers.

I don't know the names of the strokes.

I can swim 1 length of Uncle Pete's pool in 5 seconds.

I don't like it. I hate it.

I like every stroke except butterfly.

Anyone can swim - even my baby brother can.

Step 4

Try out your questions on a few people.

Discussion

1 Look at the answers that Yvette's friends have given.

Which question is each person answering?

Do you think Yvette is getting the information she wants?

2 Yvette decides to write some better questions so that people will give her useful answers.

Is this new set of questions better?

SWIMMING QUESTIONS

1 Boy ☐   Girl ☐   (tick one box)

2 Is it important for everyone to be able to swim?
   Yes ☐   No ☐   Don't know ☐

3 Can you swim at least 1 width in a swimming pool?
   Yes ☐   No ☐

4 Which swimming stroke do you prefer?
   Breast stroke ☐   Front crawl ☐   Back stroke ☐   Butterfly ☐

5 How many seconds do you take to swim 25 metres? _____ seconds

Please return to Yvette Lee.

Step 5

Write your new questions.

3 Why do you think Yvette asks question 1?

4 Why does Yvette need a data collection sheet?

Yvette has started to design the data collection sheet for her survey.

It looks like this:

Data Collection Sheet

1 Boys _____ Girls _____ Totals ☐ ☐

2 Is it important for everyone to be able to swim?
   Yes _____ Totals ☐ ☐
   No _____ Totals ☐ ☐
   Don't know _____ Totals ☐ ☐

Yvette has decided to record the boys' answers in blue and the girls' in red.

Design the rest of the data collection sheet for Yvette's survey.

The survey report

Yvette has now collected the answers to her questions. She has answers from 20 boys and 20 girls. Here is her data collection sheet.

Step 6

Collect your data.

Data Collection Sheet

		Totals	
1 Boys ~~HHI HHI HHI~~ HHI	Girls ~~HHI HHI HHI~~ HHI	20	20

2 Is it important for everyone to be able to swim?

		Totals	
Yes ~~HHI HHI HHI~~ HHI	~~HHI HHI HHI~~ HHI	20	20
No		0	0
Don't know		0	0

3 Can you swim at least 1 width of a swimming pool?

		Totals	
Yes ~~HHI HHI~~ III	~~HHI HHI HHI~~	13	15
No ~~HHI~~ II	~~HHI~~	7	5

4 Which stroke do you like best?

		Totals	
Breast stroke III	~~HHI~~ IIII	3	9
Front crawl ~~HHI~~ III	IIII	8	4
Back stroke II	I	2	1
Butterfly	I	0	1

5 How many seconds do you take to swim 25 metres

22 33 35 34 35 61 51 31 24 48 43 32 66 52 38
55 43 25 47 32 46   38 24 41 35 36 24 27

Yvette talks to the swimming pool manager about her survey.

He gives her a copy of a recent magazine article.

Step 7

Find and use information from other sources.

90% of young people can swim

Do you think Yvette can use this in her report?

Now Yvette must write her report.

She starts by planning it out.

Step 8

Write your report.

Page 1 Say what I'm trying to find out. Stick in copy of questions.
 2 Question 1 answers. Question 2 answers. Pie chart or bar chart?
 3 Question 3 answers. Pie chart or bar chart?
 4 Question 4 answers. Pie chart or bar chart?
 5 Question 5 answers. Pie chart or bar chart?
 6 Conclusions.

Look at the results from question 2 of the survey.

Everyone said they thought it was important to be able to swim.

What should Yvette say about this in her report?

1 Look at the answers from question 3 of the survey.

    a) Show the girls' answers in a bar chart and a pie chart.

    b) Show the boys' answers in a bar chart and a pie chart.

    c) Which kind of chart do you think Yvette should use, and why?

2 Look at the answers from question 4 of the survey.

Why do you think the numbers do not add up to 20 for boys and 20 for girls?

3 Look at the times taken to swim 25 metres.

    a) What is the mean time for the boys and for the girls?

    b) What is the range of times for the boys and for the girls?

    c) What conclusions can you draw from your answers to a) and b)?

4 a) Copy and complete this frequency table of the times taken by the girls to swim 25 metres.

    b) Make a similar table for the boys' times.

Girls	
Seconds	Frequency
20-29	4
30-39	6
40-49	
50-59	
60-69	

Discussion

What should Yvette write in her conclusions?

Now you are ready to do a survey of your own.

Follow the 8 steps given in this chapter.

Don't be afraid to ask other people what they think about the way you are doing it.

Here are some possible topics. Use one of these, or (even better) think up a topic of special interest to you.

- *Favourite TV programmes.*

- *Do people believe in horoscopes?*

- *Attitudes to smoking.*

- *How much time do people spend playing computer games?*

Thirteen

Algebra

Making connections

Kim is filling up her petrol tank.

She looks at the display on the petrol pump.

After a few seconds the display looks like this:

> Kim has put 2 litres of petrol in her tank

02 litres
£ 0120

> The price so far is £1.20

A little while later it looks like this:

> Now Kim has put 11 litres in her tank

11 litres
£ 0660

> The price is £6.60

When Kim has finished the display looks like this:

18 litres
£ 1080

How much petrol has Kim put in her tank?

How much will it cost her?

While she fills her tank, Kim can watch the amount of petrol increasing.

As the amount increases, so does the price.

The connection between the amount and the price is shown in this arrow diagram.

What is the price of 3 litres of petrol?

How many litres do you get for 360 pence?

Number of litres	Price in pence
1	60
2	120
3	180
4	240
5	300
6	360
7	420
8	480
9	540
10	600

1 At the petrol pump on the opposite page, what is the price of a litre of petrol?

2 Draw an arrow diagram for petrol priced at 70 pence per litre. Put the number of litres on the left, and the price in pence on the right. (Go up to 10 litres.)

3 Draw an arrow diagram for this parking meter.

Put the number of hours on the left, and the price in pence on the right. (Go up to 4 hours.)

4 These diagrams show the prices of different items at a fruit and vegetable stall. Copy and complete each diagram.

a)

Potatoes

kg	£
1	→ 0.20
2	→ 0.40
3	→ 0.60
4	→ …….
5	→ …….

b)

Apples

kg	£
1	→ …….
2	→ 1.00
3	→ …….
4	→ 2.00
5	→ 2.50

c)

Bananas

kg	£
1	→ …….
2	→ …….
3	→ 1.20
4	→ …….
5	→ 2.00

5 Thomas is doing a sponsored swim. He has lots of sponsors.

He will raise £2.50 for every length that he swims.

a) Draw an arrow diagram with the number of lengths on the left and the amount of money raised on the right. (Go up to 20 lengths.)

b) Thomas swims 18 lengths. How much money does he raise?

Look in a car magazine.

Find a model of car that you like.

Write down its fuel consumption in miles per gallon (mpg).

Write down its fuel tank capacity in gallons.

Draw an arrow diagram showing how far the car can travel on 1 gallon, 2 gallons, 3 gallons … up to a full tank of fuel.

Finding a formula

Here is the arrow diagram for the petrol pump again. It shows the connection between the number of litres and the price.

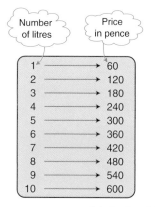

Each time you follow an arrow you multiply by 60.

$$1 \xrightarrow{\boxed{\times 60}} 60$$
$$2 \xrightarrow{\boxed{\times 60}} 120$$

You can see that to find the price (in pence) you multiply the number of litres by 60.

You can write this as

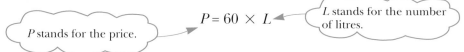

P stands for the price.

$$P = 60 \times L$$

L stands for the number of litres.

This is called a **formula** for *P*.

You can use the formula to find the price of any number of litres of petrol.

For example, if $L = 9$, $P = 60 \times 9 = 540$.

....

The price of 9 litres is 540 pence.

....

The formula is more useful than the arrow diagram, because you can use it for any number of litres.

What is the price of 12 litres of petrol?

Putting $L = 12$ in the formula gives $P = 60 \times 12 = 720$.

....

The price of 12 litres is 720 pence.

....

How would you work out the price of

a) $\frac{1}{2}$ *litre of petrol?*   *b)* $4\frac{1}{2}$ *litres of petrol?*

1 Here is the completed arrow diagram for the potatoes on page 119.

a) Copy and complete this sentence:

'To find the price (in £) you multiply the weight by ...'

b) Copy and complete this formula for the price:

$P = ... \times W$

c) Use the formula to work out the price of 12 kg of potatoes.

Potatoes

kg		£
1	⟶	0.20
2	⟶	0.40
3	⟶	0.60
4	⟶	0.80
5	⟶	1.00

2 Draw an arrow diagram for each formula.

(They have been started for you.)

a) $y = 3 \times x$

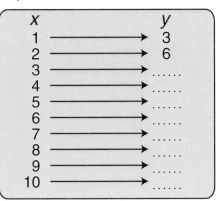

b) $B = A + 3$

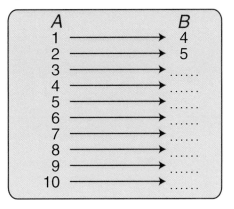

3 You saw opposite that when petrol costs 60 pence a litre, the formula

$P = 60 \times L$

gives the price, P pence, of L litres of petrol.

a) Find the price of 5 litres of petrol.

b) Find the price of 12 litres of petrol.

c) How much petrol can you buy for £6.00?

d) How much petrol can you buy for £18.00?

e) The price of petrol is increased to 70 pence a litre. Write down the new formula for P.

You are working on a market stall.

You decide to write out arrow diagrams to help you to work out customers' bills quickly.

Here is the one for grapefruits.

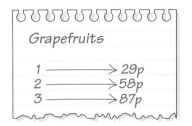

Find typical prices for oranges and for punnets of strawberries.

Draws arrow diagrams for each of these.

Conversion graphs

The ferry's speed is 17 knots.

One knot is one nautical mile per hour.

A nautical mile is about 1.2 miles, so 1 knot is about 1.2 miles per hour.

LADIES AND GENTLEMEN WELCOME ABOARD! WE ARE TRAVELLING AT A STEADY SPEED OF 17 KNOTS

You can use this table to convert between knots and miles per hour.

knots	5	10	15	20	25	30	35	40
mph	6	12	18	24	30	36	42	48

What is 15 knots in miles per hour (mph)?

What is 30 mph in knots?

What is 17 knots in mph?

It is not easy to use the table to convert 17 knots into miles per hour. 17 knots is not shown in the table.

A conversion graph like this is better.

You can use it to convert any speed (up to 40 knots).

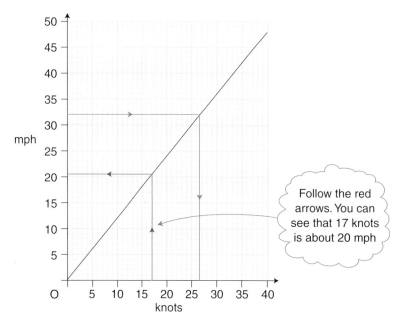

Follow the red arrows. You can see that 17 knots is about 20 mph

Use the graph to convert 32 mph to knots. (Follow the green arrows.)

Use the graph to convert 36 knots into mph.

How would you convert 45 knots into miles per hour?

This graph is on display at a bureau de change. It tells you how many US dollars ($) you will get for any number of pounds sterling (£).

1 Use the graph to work out how many dollars you will get for

a) £10   b) £25   c) £50   d) £80

2 Use the graph to work out how many pounds you will get for

a) $32   b) $48   c) $144   d) $160

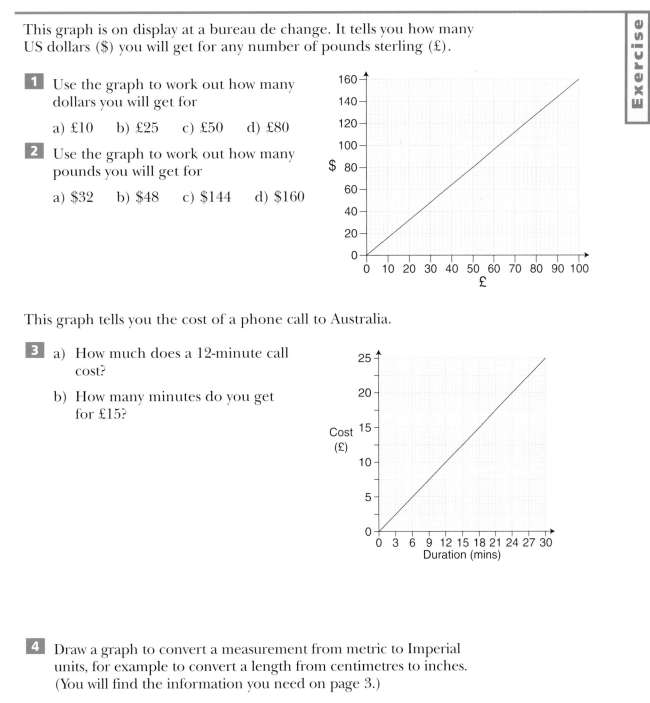

This graph tells you the cost of a phone call to Australia.

3 a) How much does a 12-minute call cost?

b) How many minutes do you get for £15?

4 Draw a graph to convert a measurement from metric to Imperial units, for example to convert a length from centimetres to inches. (You will find the information you need on page 3.)

Babies are sometimes weighed in pounds and sometimes in kilograms.

Draw a chart that health visitors and parents can use to convert babies' weights from one to the other.

Make sure your chart covers a sensible range of weights for babies up to 1 year old.

Finishing off

Now that you have finished this chapter you should

★ know what a formula is

★ be able to draw arrow diagrams

★ be able to write a simple formula

★ be able to use a formula to work out values

★ be able to use conversion graphs

Use the questions in the next exercise to check that you understand everything.

Mixed exercise

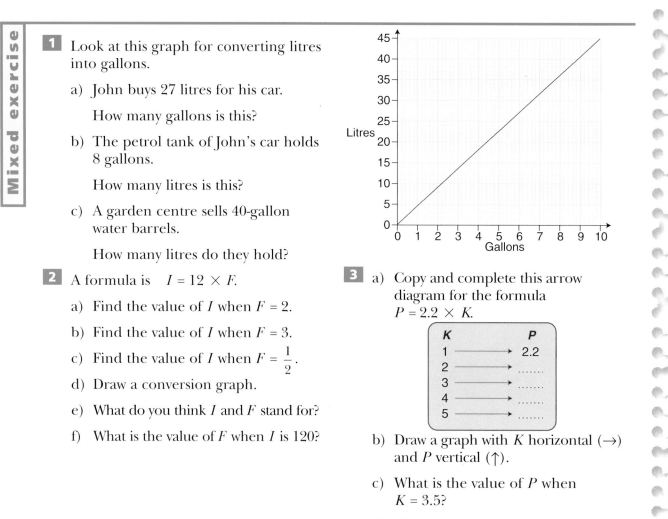

1 Look at this graph for converting litres into gallons.

a) John buys 27 litres for his car.

How many gallons is this?

b) The petrol tank of John's car holds 8 gallons.

How many litres is this?

c) A garden centre sells 40-gallon water barrels.

How many litres do they hold?

2 A formula is $I = 12 \times F$.

a) Find the value of I when $F = 2$.

b) Find the value of I when $F = 3$.

c) Find the value of I when $F = \frac{1}{2}$.

d) Draw a conversion graph.

e) What do you think I and F stand for?

f) What is the value of F when I is 120?

3 a) Copy and complete this arrow diagram for the formula $P = 2.2 \times K$.

K		P
1	→	2.2
2	→	....
3	→	....
4	→	....
5	→	....

b) Draw a graph with K horizontal ($\rightarrow$) and P vertical ($\uparrow$).

c) What is the value of P when $K = 3.5$?

d) What is the value of K when $P = 5.5$?

e) What do you think P and K stand for?

4 London and Moscow are in different time zones.

The arrow diagram shows some times in London and Moscow.

a) What is the time in Moscow when it is 1800 in London?

b) Say, in words, how you convert from London time to Moscow time.

c) Write down a formula that means the same thing as your answer to part b).

d) What is the time in London when it is 1000 in Moscow?

e) Write down a formula to convert from Moscow time to London time.

f) It is 2200 on Monday in London. What time and what day is it in Moscow?

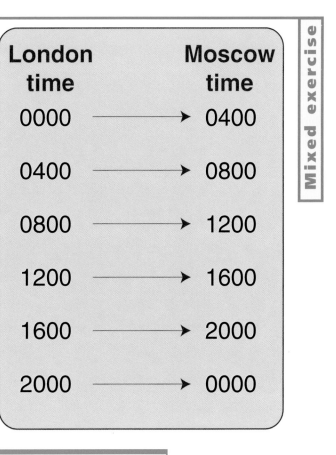

London time		Moscow time
0000	$\longrightarrow$	0400
0400	$\longrightarrow$	0800
0800	$\longrightarrow$	1200
1200	$\longrightarrow$	1600
1600	$\longrightarrow$	2000
2000	$\longrightarrow$	0000

A length of 38 mm is almost exactly the same as $1\frac{1}{2}$ inches.

Draw a graph for converting millimetres to inches.

What other lengths in millimetres convert into convenient numbers of inches?

On some kettles you can see the amount of water in them.

It is shown on a scale marked in numbers of cups.

By putting measured amounts of water into a kettle like this, find how much you need for 1, 2, 3, … cups.

Draw a conversion graph for the measured volume of water to the number of cups.

Find a formula connecting the number of cups, N, to the volume, V.

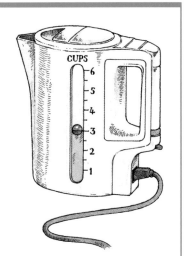

Fourteen

Travel graphs

Distance and time

Tina rides the 9 miles to work on her scooter.

One morning she sets off at 8 am as usual, but she runs out of petrol on the way.

She has to push her scooter back to a petrol station she has just passed. After filling up the tank, she continues her journey to work.

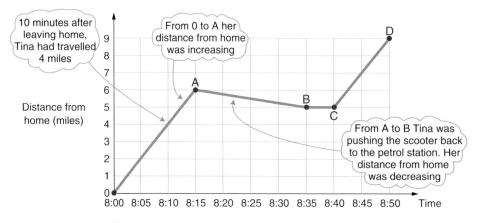

This graph shows Tina's distance from home at different times during the journey.

It is a **travel graph**.

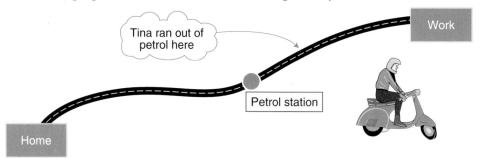

 What was happening from B to C?

What was happening from C to D?

How far had Tina travelled when she ran out of petrol at A?

How long did she take to travel that distance?

From the graph, point A is 6 miles from home, and Tina reaches point A at 8.15 am.

It has taken her 15 minutes to travel 6 miles.

126

Look again at the travel graph for Tina's journey to work.

1 How long does Tina spend at the petrol station?

2 How long does Tina's journey to work take, from beginning to end?

3 How long do you think it would take her if she didn't run out of petrol?

Explain your answer.

This travel graph shows Jonah's journey from London to Dover.

4 Jonah travelled non-stop except for a break at a service station.

What time was it when he stopped at the service station?

5 Jonah arrived at Dover at 12.15 pm. How far had he travelled?

6 How long did Jonah spend

a) driving?   b) at the service station?

7 The graph shows Jonah's distance from London.

Sketch the graph of his distance from Dover. (Do not do any measuring).

Leo plans to visit relations in Inverness. These travel graphs are for the different types of transport he could use.

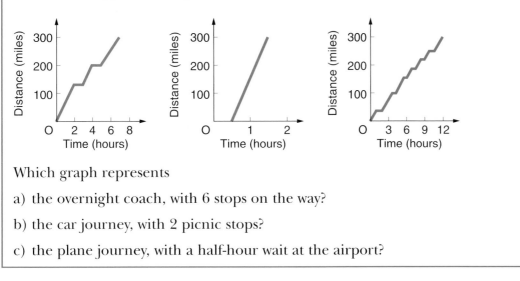

Which graph represents

a) the overnight coach, with 6 stops on the way?

b) the car journey, with 2 picnic stops?

c) the plane journey, with a half-hour wait at the airport?

Finding the speed from a travel graph

This graph shows Lucy's journey from home to school.

She walks from home to the bus stop, waits, then catches the bus to school.

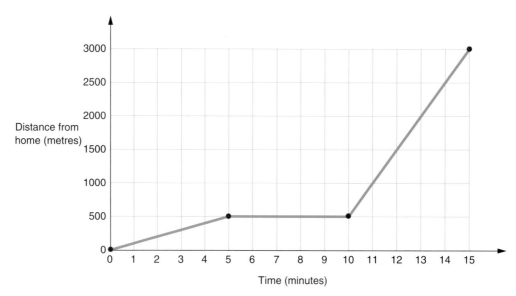

You can see that she takes 5 minutes to walk to the bus stop.

The bus stop is 500 m from home.

What is Lucy's walking speed in metres per minute?

Lucy walks 500 m in 5 minutes.

In 1 minute she walks $\frac{1}{5}$ of this.

$\frac{1}{5} \times 500 = 100$
Lucy walks at 100 metres per minute.

Another way to work this out is to use the formula

$$\text{speed} = \frac{\text{distance}}{\text{time}}$$

Lucy's speed $= \dfrac{500 \text{ m}}{5 \text{ minutes}}$

$= 100 \text{ m/minute}$

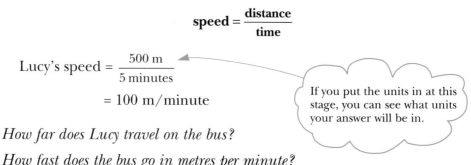

If you put the units in at this stage, you can see what units your answer will be in.

How far does Lucy travel on the bus?

How fast does the bus go in metres per minute?

How fast is this in km/h?

Beth and her friends are on holiday.

They walk along the coast path to a nearby fishing village. They have lunch in the village and then return to their resort.

This is the travel graph for the trip.

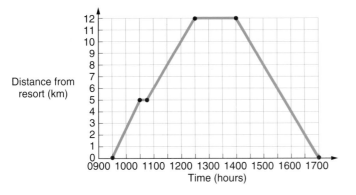

1   At what time did Beth and her friends set off on the walk?

2   a)   How far did they walk before they had a rest?

    b)   How long did it take them to walk this far?

    c)   What was their walking speed in km/h before their rest?

3   After their rest, they walked the rest of the way without stopping.

    a)   How far was this?

    b)   How long did it take?

    c)   What was their walking speed in km/h on this stretch?

4   What was their walking speed on the return journey?

Look at these 3 travel graphs.

Work out the speed in each one.

Give an example of a type of transport that could do each speed.

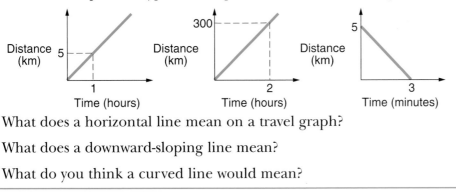

What does a horizontal line mean on a travel graph?

What does a downward-sloping line mean?

What do you think a curved line would mean?

Drawing travel graphs

An athletics coach is discussing tactics with a young 400 m runner.

The coach records the runner's time every 100 m over a practice run.

DISTANCE (metres)	100	200	300	400
TIME (seconds)	20	32	44	65

They decide it will be helpful to see this on a travel graph. To draw this they must:

- remember that time goes along (*x* axis) and distance goes up (*y* axis),

- choose suitable scales.

Their graph paper is 18 cm wide.

They need to fit 65 seconds along the time axis.

They decide to make 1 cm represent 5 seconds.

This uses about 13 cm ($13 \times 5 = 65$).

They have space to spare, but it is better to use an easy scale like this than a difficult one that uses the full width of the paper.

 What scale do they use on the distance axis?

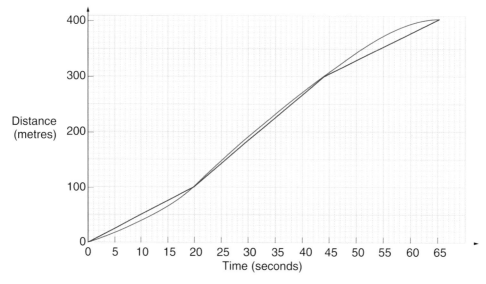

The coach uses straight lines to draw the graph in blue. This makes it look as though the runner did each 100 m at constant speed.

The runner says that is not right and draws the red graph.

 Which do you think is better?

1 Mr Smith walks to the newsagent each morning to buy a paper.

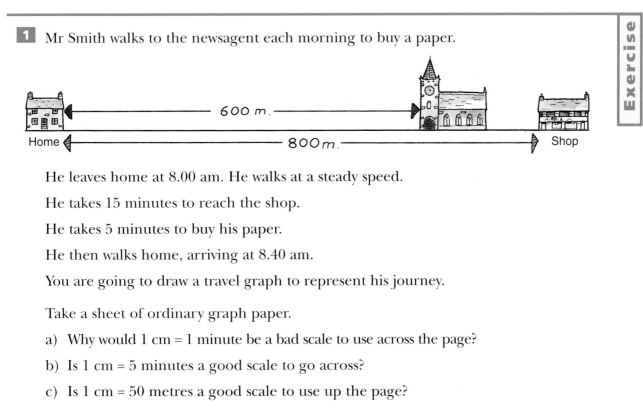

He leaves home at 8.00 am. He walks at a steady speed.

He takes 15 minutes to reach the shop.

He takes 5 minutes to buy his paper.

He then walks home, arriving at 8.40 am.

You are going to draw a travel graph to represent his journey.

Take a sheet of ordinary graph paper.

a) Why would 1 cm = 1 minute be a bad scale to use across the page?

b) Is 1 cm = 5 minutes a good scale to go across?

c) Is 1 cm = 50 metres a good scale to use up the page?

d) Draw the graph.

e) When does Mr Smith pass the church? (There are 2 answers.)

2 Aloke leaves home for work at 6.00 am.

He walks 1 mile to the bus stop, arriving at 6.15 am. He walks at a steady speed.

He waits 5 minutes for the bus.

The bus journey is 5 miles long and takes 10 minutes.

Aloke gets off the bus and walks another mile, arriving at work at 6.45 am.

a) Draw a travel graph to illustrate Aloke's journey.

b) How fast (in miles per hour) does Aloke walk?

c) How fast does the bus travel?

Obtain information about the lap times for a real athlete running a race.

Draw a travel graph.

Write a short commentary about the athlete's speed during the race.

Finishing off

> **Now that you have finished this chapter you should**
>
> ★ be able to read distance and time information from a travel graph
>
> ★ be able to work out speed from a travel graph
>
> ★ know that the slope of a travel graph represents speed

Use the questions in the next exercise to check that you understand everything.

Mixed exercise

1 This travel graph shows Hannah's journey to work.

She runs part of the way (because she is a bit late) and walks the rest.

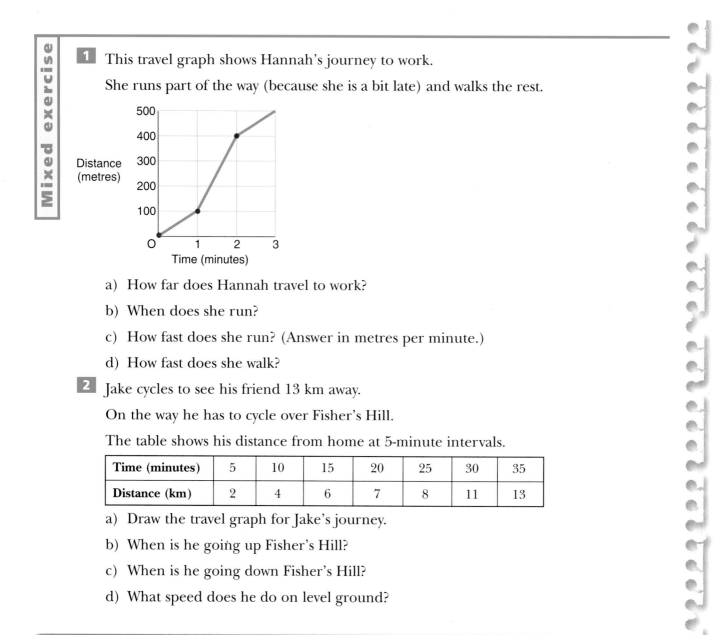

a) How far does Hannah travel to work?

b) When does she run?

c) How fast does she run? (Answer in metres per minute.)

d) How fast does she walk?

2 Jake cycles to see his friend 13 km away.

On the way he has to cycle over Fisher's Hill.

The table shows his distance from home at 5-minute intervals.

Time (minutes)	5	10	15	20	25	30	35
Distance (km)	2	4	6	7	8	11	13

a) Draw the travel graph for Jake's journey.

b) When is he going up Fisher's Hill?

c) When is he going down Fisher's Hill?

d) What speed does he do on level ground?

Travel graphs

3 This travel graph shows a race between Anwar (red) and Greg (blue).

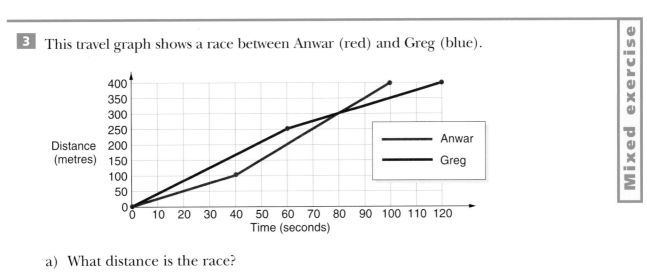

a) What distance is the race?

b) Who wins the race?

c) What does he win by (distance and time)?

4 The graph shows a swimming race between Emma (red) and Ruth (blue).

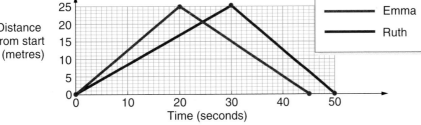

a) How many lengths is the race?

b) What distance is it?

c) Who wins the race?

d) What is Emma's speed on the first length?

e) What is Ruth's speed on the first length?

You will need a train ticket and a stop-watch.

If you look out of a train window you will see a post every mile.

Keep a record of the times at which the train goes past 5 of these.

From your record, draw the travel graph.

How fast is the train going during each mile?

Fifteen

Spending money

Bills

James moves into a new flat on 27 May. He takes electricity meter readings when he moves in and again 3 months later.

 27th May →  Units **ELECTRICITY** 2 6 4 0    Units **ELECTRICITY** 2 8 7 0 ← **27th August**

 How many units has James used?

James's bill for this quarter is shown below.

Find the 2 readings on it.

> A quarter is 3 months.

Mr J Holly 3 The Close Milton Keynes MK12 3ZQ	Account 12/89/0030 Date 30 August 1997 Cost of units 8 pence each
Reading 27 August 2 8 7 0 27 May 2 6 4 0 2 3 0	230 units at 8 p each £ 18.40 Standing charge £ 15.20 Total amount to be paid £ 33.60

You work out the number of units used by taking 2640 away from 2870.

The cost of units is 8 pence each.

James used 230 units. You work out their total cost like this:

$$
\begin{array}{r}
230 \\
\times \quad 8 \text{ pence} \\
\hline
1840 \text{ pence}
\end{array}
$$

> This is £18.40.

The standing charge does not depend on the number of units. It is £15.20 every quarter, however much electricity James uses.

The standing charge is added to the cost of the units to work out the total bill.

 Do you think that James will use the same amount of electricity in the next quarter?

Spending money

1 Here are two of Mr Jackson's gas meter readings.

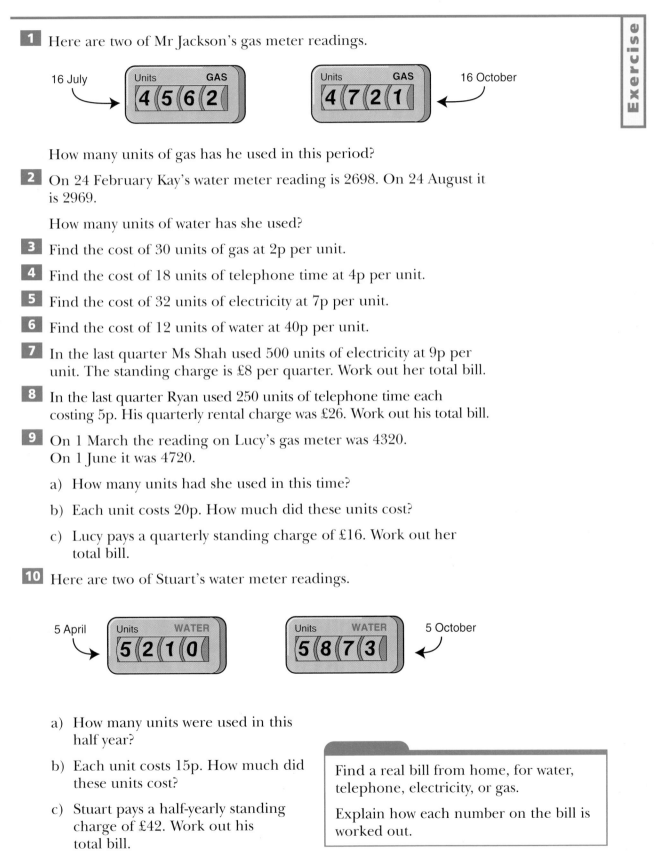

16 July

Units   GAS
4 5 6 2

Units   GAS
4 7 2 1

16 October

How many units of gas has he used in this period?

2 On 24 February Kay's water meter reading is 2698. On 24 August it is 2969.

How many units of water has she used?

3 Find the cost of 30 units of gas at 2p per unit.

4 Find the cost of 18 units of telephone time at 4p per unit.

5 Find the cost of 32 units of electricity at 7p per unit.

6 Find the cost of 12 units of water at 40p per unit.

7 In the last quarter Ms Shah used 500 units of electricity at 9p per unit. The standing charge is £8 per quarter. Work out her total bill.

8 In the last quarter Ryan used 250 units of telephone time each costing 5p. His quarterly rental charge was £26. Work out his total bill.

9 On 1 March the reading on Lucy's gas meter was 4320.
On 1 June it was 4720.

a) How many units had she used in this time?

b) Each unit costs 20p. How much did these units cost?

c) Lucy pays a quarterly standing charge of £16. Work out her total bill.

10 Here are two of Stuart's water meter readings.

5 April

Units   WATER
5 2 1 0

Units   WATER
5 8 7 3

5 October

a) How many units were used in this half year?

b) Each unit costs 15p. How much did these units cost?

c) Stuart pays a half-yearly standing charge of £42. Work out his total bill.

Find a real bill from home, for water, telephone, electricity, or gas.

Explain how each number on the bill is worked out.

Buy now, pay later

Hire purchase

Harry wants to buy this satellite dish.

He does not have enough money to pay for it all at once.

£290 OR
12 monthly payments
of only £30

He can choose to pay £30 a month for the next 12 months.

How much will this cost?

....

Total cost = 12 × £30 = £360

....

The cash price is £290. How much extra would Harry pay?

Bank loan

The extra amount seems a lot to Harry. He decides to find out about a loan.

Harry already has £90 so he needs a loan of £200.

The bank will let him repay it over 6 months, 12 months or 18 months.

This table shows the monthly repayments in each case.

Period of loan	6 months	12 months	18 months
Monthly repayment	£40	£22	£16

Harry decides to repay the loan over 6 months.

What will be the cost of repaying the loan?

....

Total repayment = £40 × 6 = £240

....

Harry works out the total cost of the dish like this:

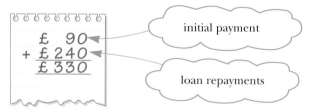

initial payment

loan repayments

Should Harry agree to the 12 monthly payments of £30 or take the loan?

Caution: Harry must be very careful about taking on a deal like this. If he fails to make the monthly payments, he may lose both the satellite dish and the money he has already paid.

In questions 1 to 4 work out

a)   the cost of the item spread over 24 months
b)   the extra amount paid.

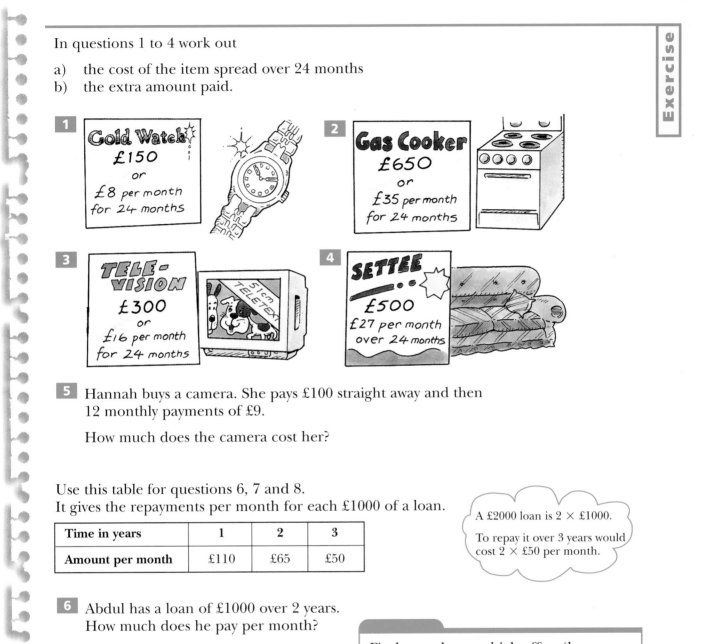

1
Gold Watch
£150
or
£8 per month
for 24 months

2
Gas Cooker
£650
or
£35 per month
for 24 months

3
TELE-VISION
£300
or
£16 per month
for 24 months

4
SETTEE
£500
£27 per month
over 24 months

5   Hannah buys a camera. She pays £100 straight away and then 12 monthly payments of £9.

How much does the camera cost her?

Use this table for questions 6, 7 and 8.
It gives the repayments per month for each £1000 of a loan.

Time in years	1	2	3
Amount per month	£110	£65	£50

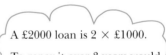

A £2000 loan is 2 × £1000.

To repay it over 3 years would cost 2 × £50 per month.

6   Abdul has a loan of £1000 over 2 years.
How much does he pay per month?

7   Kate has a loan of £1000 over 3 years.
How much does she pay

a) each month?
b) over the 3 years?

8   James has a loan of £5000 over 1 year.
How much does he pay

a) each month?
b) over the year?

Find a catalogue which offers 'buy now, pay later' deals.

Choose an item that you would like to buy.

Compare the cash price with the total price to be paid over a period.

Can you find a better deal in the shops?

Write a short report on the different deals you can find. Which would you choose, and why?

Value added tax (VAT)

VAT is a tax that you pay whenever you buy something.

Only a few types of purchase are exempt from VAT.

? *Find out the present rate of VAT.*

Find out what types of item are exempt.

Example

Look at these two deals on the same hi-fi.

Which store offers the better deal if VAT is 17.5%?

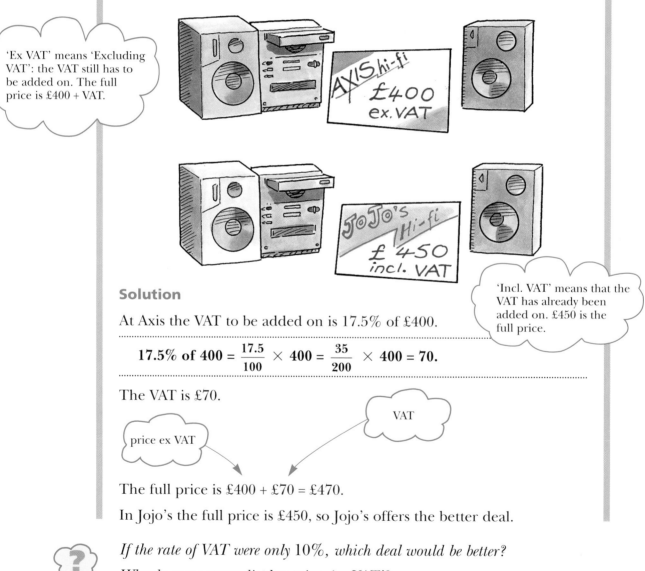

'Ex VAT' means 'Excluding VAT': the VAT still has to be added on. The full price is £400 + VAT.

'Incl. VAT' means that the VAT has already been added on. £450 is the full price.

Solution

At Axis the VAT to be added on is 17.5% of £400.

$$\textbf{17.5\% of 400} = \frac{17.5}{100} \times 400 = \frac{35}{200} \times 400 = 70.$$

The VAT is £70.

price ex VAT   VAT

The full price is £400 + £70 = £470.

In Jojo's the full price is £450, so Jojo's offers the better deal.

? *If the rate of VAT were only 10%, which deal would be better?*

Why do some stores display prices 'ex VAT'?

In questions 1 to 4 the price of each item is given excluding VAT.

VAT is to be added at 17.5%.

Work out

a) the amount of VAT   b) the price including VAT.

1 £120 ex VAT

2 £180 ex VAT

4 £900 ex VAT

3 CAR SERVICE £80 ex VAT

5 In Store A an office chair is priced at £60 ex VAT. In Store B it is priced at £75 incl VAT at 17.5%.

Which store offers the better deal and by how much?

6 In Store X a computer printer is priced at £215 ex VAT. In Store Y it is priced at £255 incl VAT at 17.5%.

Which store offers the better deal and by how much?

The filing cabinet in question 1 is priced at £120 ex VAT. The shop assistant works out the VAT at 17.5% as follows.

```
£120  ÷  10  =  £12.00
      ÷   2  =  £ 6.00
      ÷   2  =  £ 3.00
                £21.00
```

a) Why does this method work?

b) How could the assistant work out VAT if the rate were changed to 15% or 25%?

Write out your calculation for the £120 filing cabinet in each case.

Finishing off

> **Now that you have finished this chapter you should be able to**
>
> ★ work out household bills ★ work out VAT
>
> ★ work out the costs of 'buy
>   now, pay later' deals

Use the questions in the next exercise to check that you understand everything.

Mixed exercise

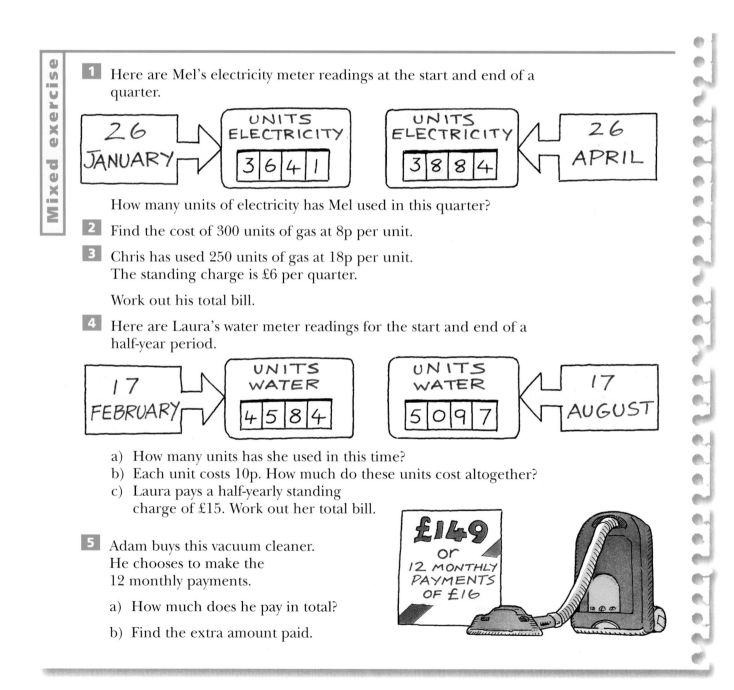

1 Here are Mel's electricity meter readings at the start and end of a quarter.

26 JANUARY → UNITS ELECTRICITY 3 6 4 1   UNITS ELECTRICITY 3 8 8 4 ← 26 APRIL

How many units of electricity has Mel used in this quarter?

2 Find the cost of 300 units of gas at 8p per unit.

3 Chris has used 250 units of gas at 18p per unit.
The standing charge is £6 per quarter.

Work out his total bill.

4 Here are Laura's water meter readings for the start and end of a half-year period.

17 FEBRUARY → UNITS WATER 4 5 8 4   UNITS WATER 5 0 9 7 ← 17 AUGUST

a) How many units has she used in this time?
b) Each unit costs 10p. How much do these units cost altogether?
c) Laura pays a half-yearly standing
   charge of £15. Work out her total bill.

5 Adam buys this vacuum cleaner.
He chooses to make the
12 monthly payments.

a) How much does he pay in total?

b) Find the extra amount paid.

£149
or
12 MONTHLY
PAYMENTS
OF £16

6 Jill buys a CD player priced at £99. She pays £30 straight away, then 12 monthly payments of £7.50.

How much does she pay in total?

Use this table to answer questions 7, 8 and 9.

It shows the amount to pay each month on loans of £500, £1000 and £5000.

Repayment period	Amount of loan		
	£500	**£1000**	**£5000**
2 years	£30	£56	£275
3 years	£22	£41	£200
4 years	£18	£35	£170

7 Ms Patel has a loan of £500 to be repaid over 2 years.

How much does she pay each month?

8 Mr Sou has a loan of £5000 to be repaid over 3 years.

How much does he pay each month?

9 Miss Hansen has a loan of £1000 to be repaid over 4 years.

a) How much does she pay each month?

b) How much will she pay in total over 4 years?

10 A CD midi system costs £200 excluding VAT. VAT is added at 17.5%.

Work out how much VAT is added.

11 A video recorder costs £150 excluding VAT. VAT is added at 17.5%.

What is the total cost?

12 A computer is offered for sale in two stores as shown. VAT is 17.5%.

Which store offers the better deal and by how much?

Using information from catalogues or magazines, work out the cost of buying the complete computer system of your choice.

Give the price both ex VAT and inc VAT.

You have a price limit of £2000.

Sixteen

Perimeter and area

Perimeter

This is a plan of the Anderson family's living room.

Mr Anderson is going to redecorate the living room.

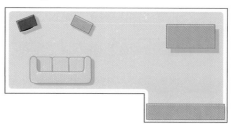

He wants to know how far it is round the edge of the room so that he can work out how many rolls of wallpaper to buy.

The distance around the edge of a shape is called the **perimeter**.

Mr Anderson measures the length of most of the walls and writes them on a plan of the room.

He cannot measure the wall behind the sideboard very easily.

He works out its length from the plan.

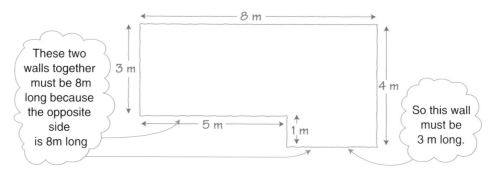

These two walls together must be 8m long because the opposite side is 8m long

So this wall must be 3 m long.

Mr Anderson puts the 3 metre length on his diagram.

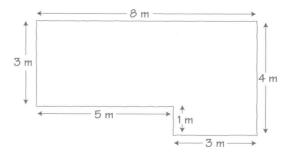

Now he can work out the perimeter of the room.

....

Perimeter = 8 + 3 + 5 + 1 + 3 + 4 = 24
The distance round the room is 24 metres.

....

1 Use a ruler to measure the perimeters of these shapes.

a)

b)

2 Work out the perimeters of these shapes. (Do not do any measuring.)

a)

4 cm

7 cm

b)

10 cm

9 cm

4 cm

6 cm

c)

3·7 cm

6·8 cm

2·4 cm

8·5 cm

d)

1·9 cm

3·4 cm

4·1 cm

2·1 cm

5·6 cm

4·9 cm

3 A farmer wants to put a fence round this field.

Fencing costs £12.40 per metre.

How much will the fence cost?

53 m

34 m

41 m

21 m

25 m

76 m

Find the perimeter of one of the rooms in your home.

Wallpaper is usually sold in rolls 52 cm wide.

Each roll is usually long enough to provide 3 strips of wallpaper.

Work out how many rolls of wallpaper would be needed to paper the whole room.

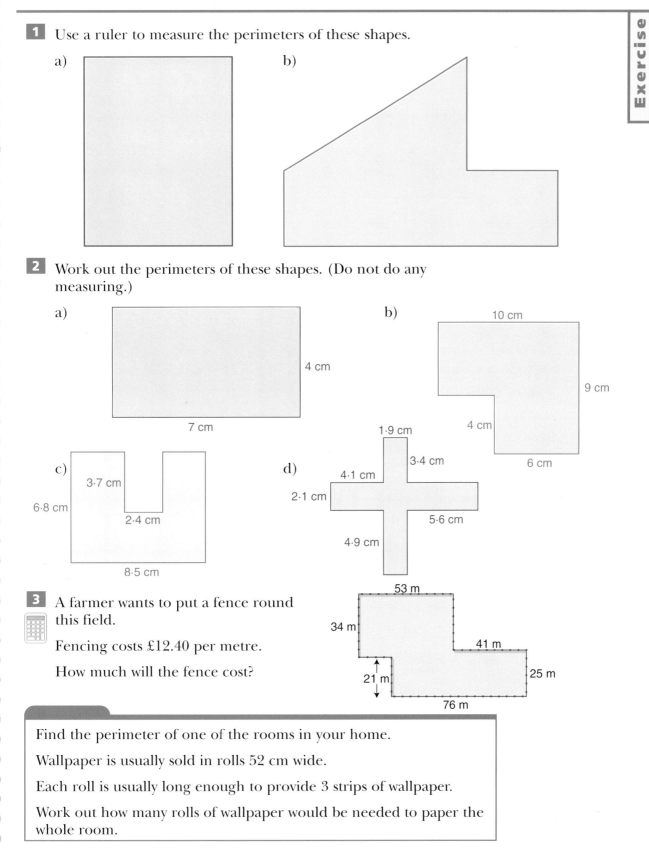

Area

Sarah is laying some paving slabs to make a patio.

This is her plan for the patio.

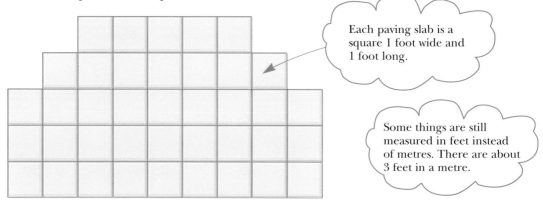

Each paving slab is a square 1 foot wide and 1 foot long.

Some things are still measured in feet instead of metres. There are about 3 feet in a metre.

Each paving slab has an **area** of 1 square foot.

Area is the amount of space inside a shape.

There are 39 slabs on the plan altogether.

Area of the patio = 39 square feet.

Sarah also wants to put some grass seed on her lawn.

The packet tells her how many handfuls to use per square metre.

She needs to know the area of the lawn to find out how much grass seed to use.

This is Sarah's plan of the lawn.

She has drawn it on a square grid.

Each square on the grid is 1 m long and 1 m wide.

Each square has an area of 1 square metre.

You can find an estimate of the lawn area by counting the squares that are at least half covered by the lawn.

Sarah colours in the squares that are at least half covered.

When she has finished there are 20 coloured squares.

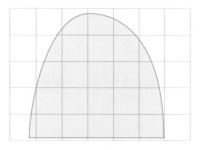

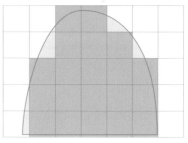

Area of the lawn = approximately 20 square metres.

1 Find the exact areas of the shapes below by counting the squares.

Each square represents 1 square centimetre (1 cm^2).

a)

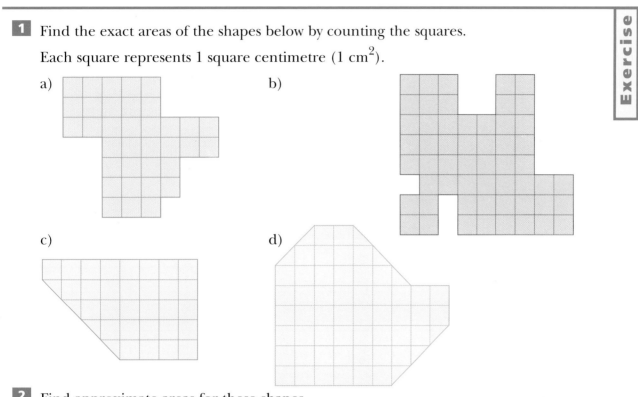

b)

c)

d)

2 Find approximate areas for these shapes.

Again each square represents 1 square centimetre.

a)

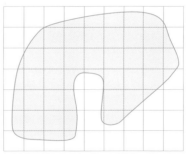

b)

3 Draw the rectangles below on to centimetre squared paper and count the squares to find their areas.

a)

7 cm

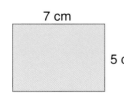

5 cm

b)

6 cm

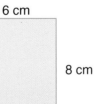

8 cm

Draw round each of your hands on centimetre squared paper and estimate the area of each hand.

Which hand is bigger?

Area of a rectangle

Here is a rectangle.

It can be split up into lots of small squares, each 1 cm long and 1 cm wide.

Each small square has an area of 1 square centimetre.

This is written 1 cm^2.

There are 4 rows of squares.

Each row has 5 squares in it.

The total number of squares is

$$4 \times 5 = 20$$

So the area of the rectangle is 20 cm^2.

The area of any rectangle can be found by multiplying the length by the width:

Area of a rectangle = length $\times$ width

Shapes made from several rectangles

This shape is not a rectangle, but you can split it up into rectangles to work out its area.

Here is one way of splitting it.

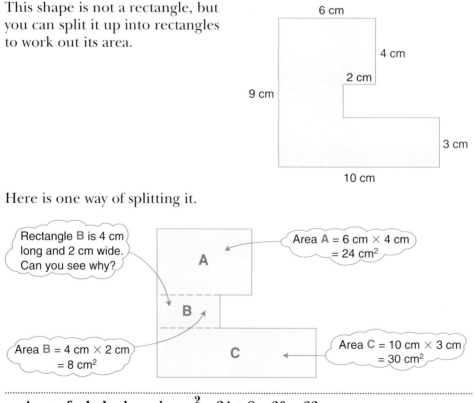

Rectangle **B** is 4 cm long and 2 cm wide. Can you see why?

Area **A** = 6 cm $\times$ 4 cm = 24 cm²

Area **B** = 4 cm $\times$ 2 cm = 8 cm²

Area **C** = 10 cm $\times$ 3 cm = 30 cm²

Area of whole shape in cm^2 = 24 + 8 + 30 = 62

1 Find the areas and perimeters of the following rectangles.

    a) Length 9 cm, width 7 cm   b) Length 12 cm, width 5 cm

    c) Length 6 m, width 11 m   d) Length 2.5 m, width 4 m

2 A jewellery designer wants to make some pendants using letters of the alphabet.

Find the area of metal she needs to make each of the letters below.

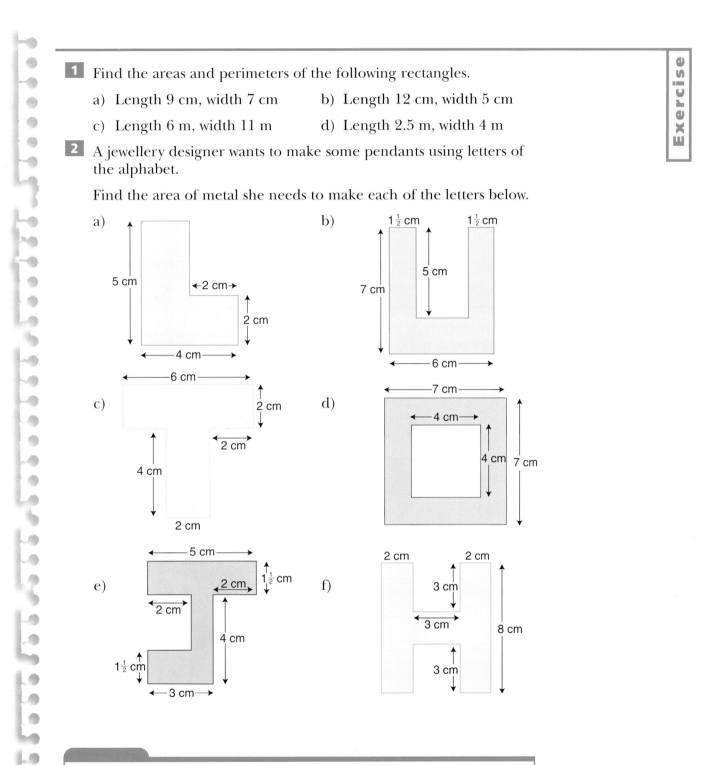

You are planning to repaint a room in your house.

Work out the area of each of the walls. Don't include doors and windows or any other areas which do not need to be painted.

Find out the cost of a tin of paint and what area it covers, and work out how much it would cost to paint the room.

Finishing off

> **Now that you have finished this chapter you should**
>
> ★ know that the perimeter of a shape is the distance round its edge
>
> ★ be able to find the perimeter of a shape with straight sides
>
> ★ know that the area of a shape is the amount of space inside it
>
> ★ know that area is measured in square units, like cm^2 or m^2
>
> ★ be able to estimate the area of a shape drawn on a grid of squares
>
> ★ be able to work out the area of a rectangle
>
> ★ be able to work out the area of a shape made from rectangles

Use the questions in the next exercise to check that you understand everything.

Mixed exercise

1 Find the area and perimeter of each of the shapes below.

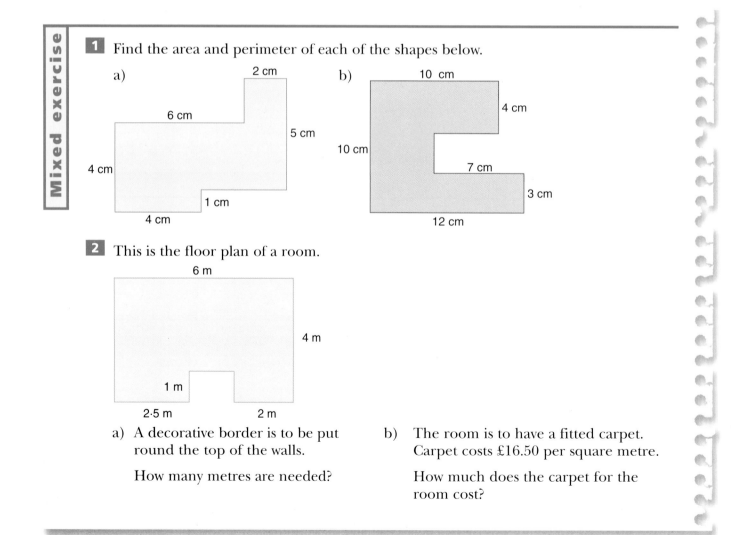

a)

2 cm
6 cm
5 cm
4 cm
1 cm
4 cm

b)

10 cm
4 cm
10 cm
7 cm
3 cm
12 cm

2 This is the floor plan of a room.

6 m
4 m
1 m
2·5 m   2 m

a) A decorative border is to be put round the top of the walls.

How many metres are needed?

b) The room is to have a fitted carpet. Carpet costs £16.50 per square metre.

How much does the carpet for the room cost?

3 The map shows a desert island.

The grid squares on the map are 1 km by 1 km.

Estimate the area of the island.

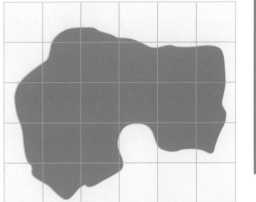

4 The squares of a chess board are 2 cm × 2 cm.

a) What is the area of one square?

b) How many squares are there on the board?

c) What is the area of all the squares together?

d) What are the length and width of the board?

e) Check that multiplying the length and width gives the same answer as you got in c).

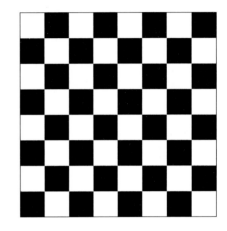

Investigation

Dennis is a farmer. He has 20 sections of fencing, each 5 metres long. He wants to use it to make an enclosure for a goat.

He could make an enclosure like this.

This would have an area of

30 m × 20 m = 600 m^2

There are lots of different shapes that Dennis could make, but he wants the goat to have as much space as possible.

Investigate the different enclosures that he could make, and find out which one has the largest area.

(The enclosures do not have to be rectangles!)

Now find out what happens if Dennis has a different number of fencing sections.

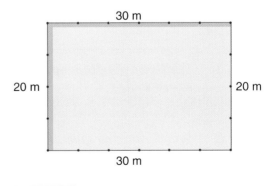

Choose a room at home and investigate the cost of redecorating and carpeting it.

You will need to decide whether to use paint or wallpaper, and find out prices and how much you will need.

Seventeen

Three dimensions

Drawing solid objects

All solid objects have three dimensions: length, width and height.

A drawing has only two dimensions: length and width.

This makes solid objects difficult to draw.

There are several ways of representing solid objects on paper. Here are three different ways of drawing the solid shape called a triangular prism.

Three-dimensional drawings

These are drawings made to look like three-dimensional objects. They may use perspective.

Nets

Nets show what the shape would look like if it could be opened up and made flat.

Views

These show what the shape looks like from the top, the front and the side.

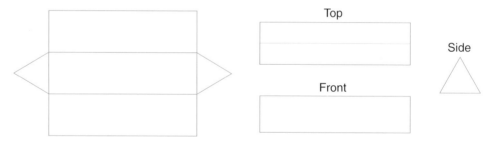

Top

Side

Front

1   *Which way of drawing the triangular prism do you think would be easiest to do?*

Which do you think would be hardest to do?

2   *Which drawing gives the best idea of what the prism really looks like?*

3   *Which drawing would be best if you wanted to make a model of the prism?*

4   *Which drawing would be best if you wanted to show the lengths of each edge of the prism?*

5   *Here is a drawing of a* **sphere**.

Is it possible to draw a net of a sphere?

What would the different views of a sphere look like?

Here are drawings of some other solid shapes.

Each set of drawings shows the same 4 solid shapes.

Match up each net and each set of views with its three-dimensional drawing.

Three-dimensional drawings

Nets

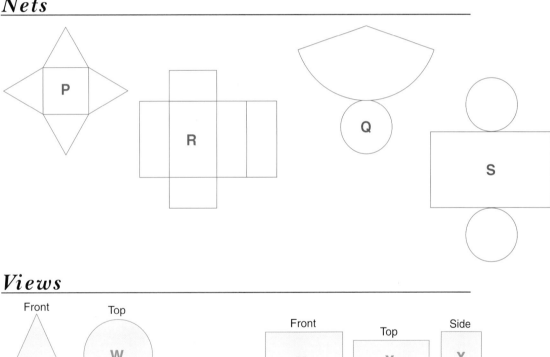

Views

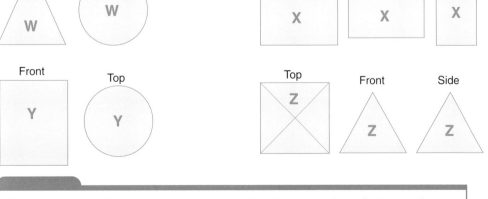

Draw the net of a model of a house. Cut it out and stick it together.

Using isometric paper

You can make drawings of three-dimensional objects using isometric paper.

It is important to make sure that you are using the paper the right way round.

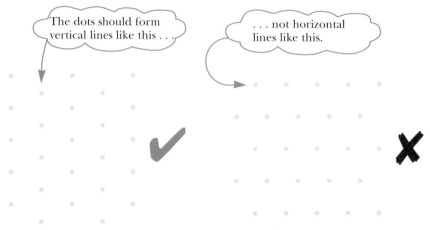

The dots should form vertical lines like this . . .

. . . not horizontal lines like this.

The simplest object to draw on isometric paper is a cube of side 1 cm.

Cubes and cuboids of different sizes are also easy to draw.

Cube of side 1 cm   **Cuboid 2 cm by 3 cm by 4 cm**

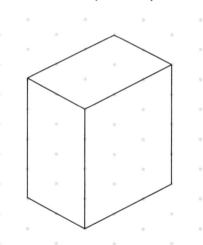

You can draw other shapes made from cubes like this.

You should only put in lines that can be seen.

This is a drawing of an arrangement of 8 cubes – 7 cubes on the bottom layer and 1 on top.

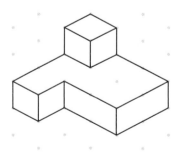

1 Draw the following shapes on isometric paper.

(Check that the paper is the right way round before you start.)

a) A cube of side 3 cm

b) A cuboid 2 cm long, 1 cm wide and 4 cm high

c) A cuboid 4 cm long, 4 cm wide and 3 cm high

2 Draw these solid shapes on isometric paper.

For each shape, write down how many cubes have been used to make it.

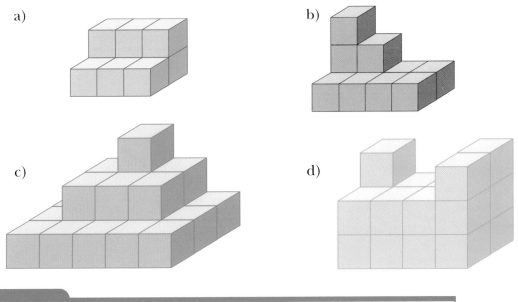

a)

b)

c)

d)

You can draw 'three-dimensional' letters of the alphabet using isometric paper.

The diagrams show how to draw the letter E.

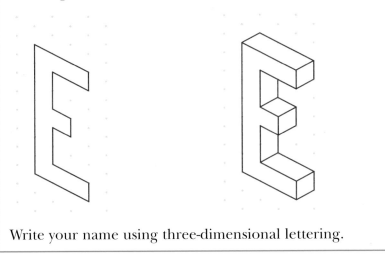

Write your name using three-dimensional lettering.

Nets

Hannah is making sweets for her friends.
She wants to put the sweets in boxes.

She has one box that is the right size.
She wants to make some more.

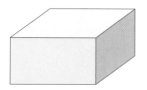

Hannah cuts down the edges of her box and flattens it out.

The flat shape that she has made is called the **net** of the box.

Hannah draws several of the nets on some card to make her boxes. She draws tabs on some of the sides, so that she will be able to glue the boxes together.

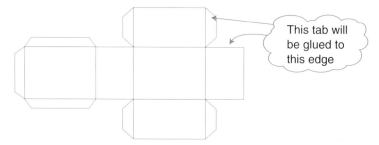

This tab will be glued to this edge

Hannah cuts out the nets, folds along the lines, and glues the tabs into place. The boxes are ready.

Faces, edges and corners

You can see by looking at the net that Hannah's box is made of 6 rectangles. These are called **faces**.

A box with 6 rectangular faces is called a **cuboid**.

If the faces are square the box is called a **cube**.

Find something in your classroom that is a cube or a cuboid.

Check that it has 6 faces.

Count the edges. There should be 12 edges.

Count the corners. A corner is called a vertex. There should be 8 vertices. (Vertices is the plural of vertex.)

1 Which of the following diagrams are nets for a cube?

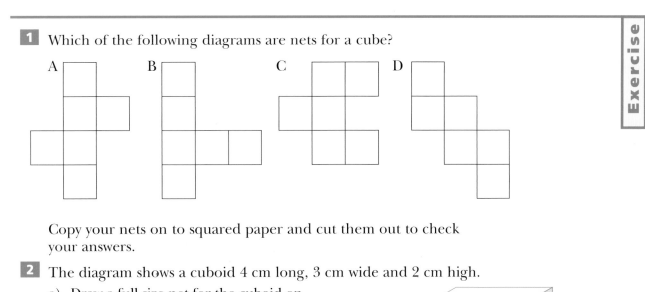

A   B   C   D

Copy your nets on to squared paper and cut them out to check your answers.

2 The diagram shows a cuboid 4 cm long, 3 cm wide and 2 cm high.

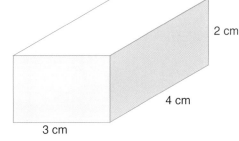

a) Draw a full size net for the cuboid on a piece of centimetre squared paper.

b) Draw tabs on the net so that it can be stuck together.

c) Cut out the net and use it to make the cuboid.

2 cm

4 cm

3 cm

3 The diagram shows the net of a solid shape.

You may like to make this solid shape by drawing the net yourself, cutting it out and glueing it together.

a) What is the name of this solid shape?

b) How many faces does it have?

c) How many edges does it have?

d) How many vertices (corners) does it have?

4 The diagram shows the net of another solid shape.

Again, you may like to make the solid shape by drawing your own net.

a) What is the name of this solid shape?

b) How many faces does it have?

c) How many edges does it have?

d) How many vertices does it have?

Design some different boxes to hold sweets and draw their nets.

What are the good points and bad points of each design? (For example, would they stack well on the shelves of a shop?)

Volume

Hassan is packing boxes into a delivery lorry.

The back of the lorry is a cuboid 3 metres wide, 2 metres high and 5 metres long.

Each box is a cube 1 metre wide, 1 metre high and 1 metre long.

Each box has a **volume** of 1 cubic metre.

This is written as 1 m^3.

The volume of a three-dimensional shape tells you how much space it takes up.

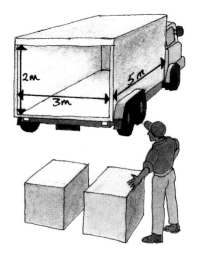

Hassan starts by putting a row of 3 boxes across the back of the lorry.

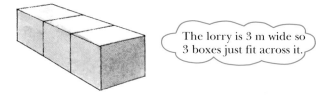

The lorry is 3 m wide so 3 boxes just fit across it.

Hassan puts another row of 3 boxes on top of the row already there.

There are 2 rows of 3 boxes, making 6 boxes altogether.

The lorry is 2 m high so 2 rows just fit on top of each other.

Hassan puts 5 stacks of boxes like the one above into the lorry.

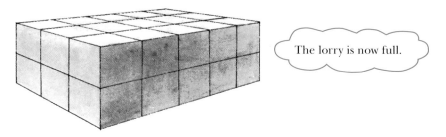

The lorry is now full.

Hassan has put 30 boxes into the lorry, so the lorry has a volume of 30 cubic metres (30 m^3).

The volume of any shape made up of cubes can be found by counting the number of cubes in the shape.

The volume of a cuboid is length × width × height.

1 Each of these stacks is made up of boxes 1 metre long, 1 metre wide and 1 metre high.

Find the volume of each stack.

a)

b)

c)

d)

2 These models are made out of centimetre cubes.

Find the volume of each model.

a)

b)

c)

d)

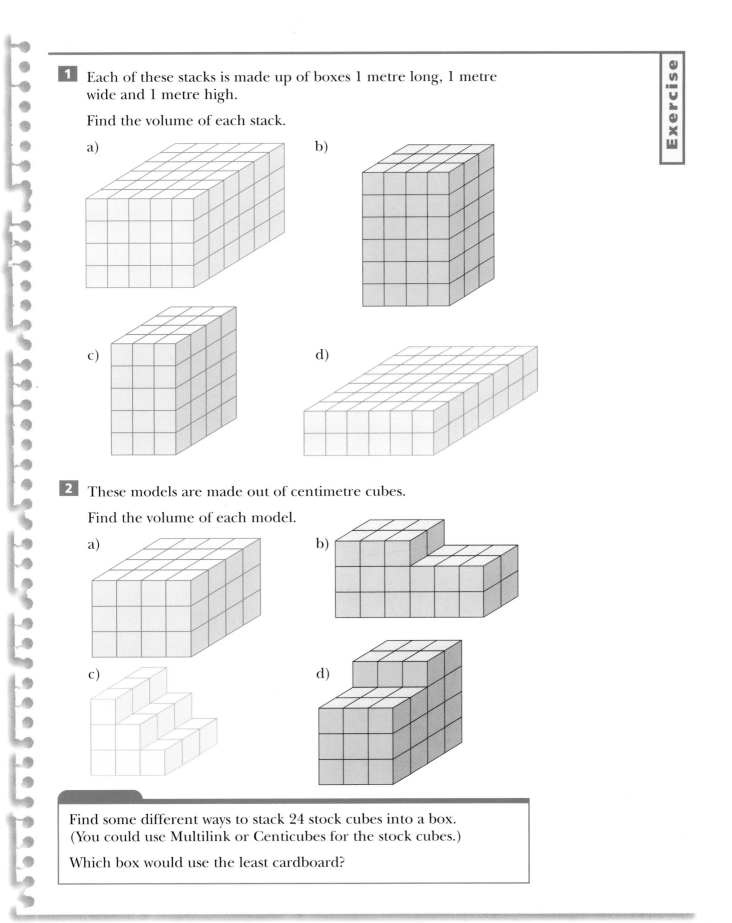

Find some different ways to stack 24 stock cubes into a box.
(You could use Multilink or Centicubes for the stock cubes.)

Which box would use the least cardboard?

Finishing off

Now that you have finished this chapter you should

★ recognise different ways of drawing solid shapes

★ be able to draw three-dimensional objects on isometric paper

★ be able to draw nets for a cube, cuboid, prism and pyramid

★ know what is meant by *faces*, *edges* and *vertices* of a solid shape

★ know that volume is measured in cubic units such as cm^3 and m^3

★ be able to find the volume of a cuboid by counting cubes

Use the questions in the next exercise to check that you understand everything.

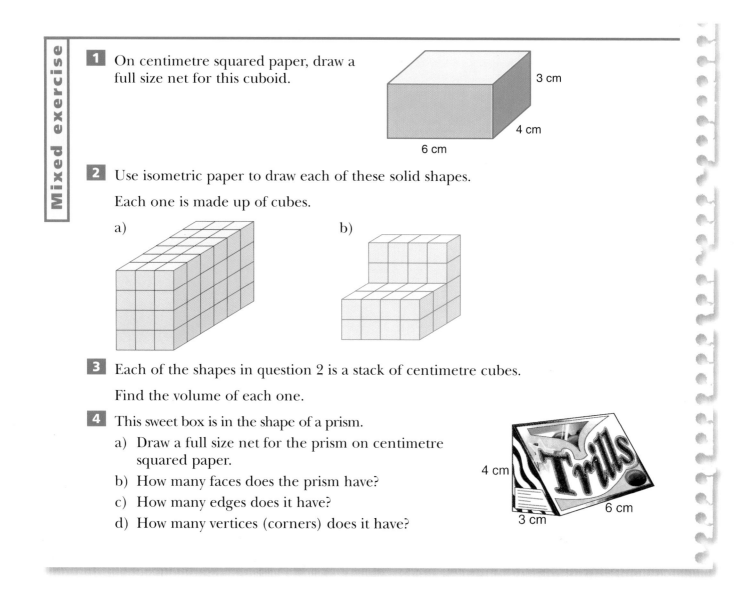

Mixed exercise

1 On centimetre squared paper, draw a full size net for this cuboid.

3 cm
4 cm
6 cm

2 Use isometric paper to draw each of these solid shapes.

Each one is made up of cubes.

a)

b)

3 Each of the shapes in question 2 is a stack of centimetre cubes.

Find the volume of each one.

4 This sweet box is in the shape of a prism.

a) Draw a full size net for the prism on centimetre squared paper.

b) How many faces does the prism have?

c) How many edges does it have?

d) How many vertices (corners) does it have?

4 cm
6 cm
3 cm

5 A company that packs tennis balls is trying out this new pyramid-shaped box.

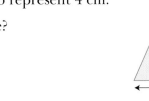

a) How many tennis balls do you think will fit in the box?

b) Draw a net for the pyramid. Use 1 cm to represent 4 cm.

c) How many faces does the pyramid have?

d) How many edges does it have?

e) How many vertices does it have?

Investigations

1 Make a table like this.

Shape	Faces	Edges	Vertices
Cuboid			

Fill in the numbers of faces, edges and vertices for any solid shapes with straight edges you can find. (You could use your answers to questions 3 and 4 on page 155. If you have Multilink or Polydron, you could use this to make some more shapes of your own.)

Try to find a rule linking the numbers of faces, edges and vertices for any shape.

2 Use Multilink or Centicubes to find as many different shapes as you can with a volume of 4 cubic units. For each shape, find the surface area (the total area of all the faces showing).

For example, try making this shape. It has 18 faces showing, so its surface area is 18 square units.

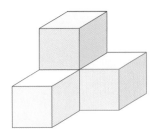

Which shape has the biggest surface area?

Which has the smallest?

Now try shapes with a volume of 5 cubic units and 6 cubic units.

Find a simple three-dimensional object such as a set of bookshelves.

Take suitable measurements, then draw it on isometric paper.

Eighteen

Earning money

Wages

Julie applies for this job and gets it.

How much will she earn each week?

Supermarket assistant
Suit school leaver
38 hour week
£4 per hour

rate per hour

number of hours

Weekly wage = £4 × 38 = £152
Julie will earn £152 per week.

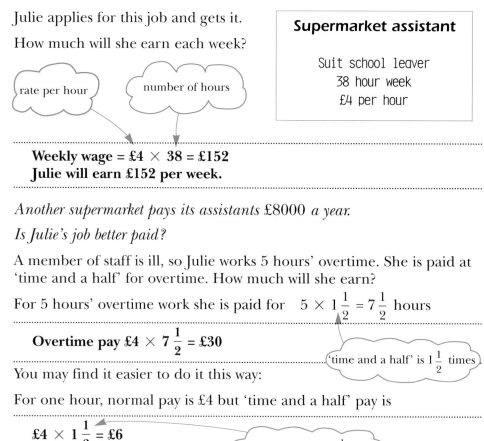

Another supermarket pays its assistants £8000 a year.

Is Julie's job better paid?

A member of staff is ill, so Julie works 5 hours' overtime. She is paid at 'time and a half' for overtime. How much will she earn?

For 5 hours' overtime work she is paid for $5 \times 1\frac{1}{2} = 7\frac{1}{2}$ hours

Overtime pay £4 × $7\frac{1}{2}$ = £30

'time and a half' is $1\frac{1}{2}$ times

You may find it easier to do it this way:

For one hour, normal pay is £4 but 'time and a half' pay is

£4 × $1\frac{1}{2}$ = £6
Overtime pay £6 × 5 = £30

'time and a half' is $1\frac{1}{2}$ times

Here is a quicker way to work out overtime pay.

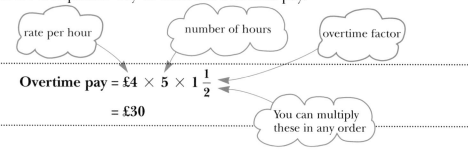

rate per hour

number of hours

overtime factor

Overtime pay = £4 × 5 × $1\frac{1}{2}$

= £30

You can multiply these in any order

On the Sunday before Christmas Julie works 6 hours' overtime which is paid at 'double time'. Use the quick method to work out how much she is paid.

1 Work out how much each person earns per week.

a) Debbie: £5 an hour for a 36-hour week.

b) Joseph: £4.50 an hour for a 20-hour week.

c) Maria: 5 days a week, £40 a day.

d) Jamie £30 per half day, for Monday morning, Tuesday afternoon and all day Friday.

2 Rosie works 3 days a week for 4 hours each day.

a) How many hours does she work in a week?

b) She is paid £5 an hour. What is her weekly wage?

3 This timesheet shows Kezi's hours of work for last week.

a) How many hours did she work on Monday?

b) How many hours did she work in the week?

c) Her pay is £4 an hour. How much did she earn for the week?

	Start	Finish	Hours
Monday	0800	1200	
Tuesday	0800	1200	
Wednesday	0800	1200	
Thursday			
Friday	0800	1200	
Saturday	0700	1200	
		Total	

4 Victoria is paid £4 an hour and works 6 hours at 'double time'.

How much does she earn?

5 Ian is paid £4.50 an hour and works 5 hours at 'time and a half'.

How much does he earn?

6 Gary earns £6.50 an hour for a 36-hour week. He does 6 hours' overtime at 'double time'.

How much does he earn in total?

7 Tara earns £5 an hour for a 37-hour week. She does 4 hours' overtime at 'time and a half'.

How much does she earn in total?

Find out how much a paperboy/girl earns per day.

How many papers are there on each round?

Is the rate of pay different on a Sunday?

How much does the customer pay each week for delivery?

Salaries

Gemma has an annual salary of £12 600. This means that Gemma earns £12 600 per year.

How much is this each month?

Gemma's pay = $\dfrac{£12\,600}{12}$ = £1050

There are 12 months in a year

Salary scales

Mitesh starts work as a trainee environmental health officer.
He is on point 1 of the scale shown below.

Point	Salary (£)
1	8400
2	8800
3	9200
4	9600
5	10 000

Starting salary

Salary after 1 year

Salary after 2 years

How much will he earn after 4 years?

Commission

Ann gets this job.

Part of her salary is based on the value of the goods she sells. This is called **commission**.

Ann sells £30 000 worth of goods one year.

What is her total salary for the year?

Ann's commission is 25% of £30 000.

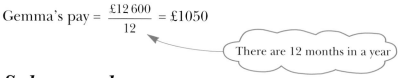

Salesperson

£10 000
plus 25% commission

25% of 30 000 $= \dfrac{25}{100} \times 30\,000 = 7500$

Ann's total salary = £10 000 + £7500

= £17 500

basic salary

commission

Ann's salary for the year is £17 500.

How much does Ann earn in total in a year when she sells £60 000 of goods?

What are the advantages of being on commission?

What are the disadvantages of being on commission?

1 Helen's salary is £9000 a year. How much is this per month?

2 Mitchell earns £820 a month. What is his annual salary?

3 Claudette and Sean do this job on a job-share basis.

This means that they each work half a week and get half the salary.

How much does Claudette earn each month?

> ## Science Technician
> **Salary £9600**
> **Suitable for job share**

4 Sacha's annual salary is £14 040.

His friend Tamara earns £255 a week.

Who earns more in a year and by how much?

5 Danielle is a trainee housing manager. She starts work on point 1 (£8400) of the salary scale opposite.

She gains one salary point each time she completes a year with her firm, and each time she passes a stage in her training.

Work out Danielle's salary

a) after 9 months

b) after 18 months, having passed Stage 1 of her training

c) after 27 months, having passed Stage 2 of her training.

6 Wesley's basic salary is £600 a month and he gets 25% commission on his sales.

His sales figures for May to August are shown below.

Month	May	June	July	August
Sales (£)	1000	1100	960	660

Calculate Wesley's total pay for each month.

7 Last year Ginette and Mark both earned a basic salary of £8000.

They both received 30% commission on their sales.

a) Ginette made sales worth £20 000. How much did she earn in total?

b) Mark made sales worth £17 500. How much did he earn in total?

> Some job advertisers say *attractive salary plus benefits*.
>
> Find out 4 examples of benefits.

Simple interest

Martyn has saved £600 and wants to invest it for 2 years in a building society. These are the interest rates offered.

Amount	Interest rate
£100–£499	3.5% p.a.
£500–£2499	4%p.a.
£2500 and over	4.25%p.a.

> p.a. means 'per annum' (each year)

Why do you think the interest rate is higher on larger amounts?

What interest will Martyn get on his £600?

£600 is between £500 and £2499 so the interest rate will be 4% p.a.

Each year Martyn's interest is

> interest rate

> Martyn's savings

$$4\% \text{ of } £600 = \frac{4}{100} \times £600 = £24$$

This £24 interest is sent to Martyn at the end of the first year.

The £600 in the account will earn another £24 during the second year.

The simple interest Martyn earns over 2 years will be

$$2 \times £24 = £48$$

> This is called **simple interest**. If the building society added the interest to the account instead, Martyn would get **compound interest**.

You can use this formula to calculate simple interest:

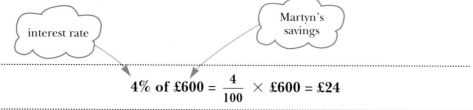

$$I = \frac{P \times R \times T}{100} = \frac{PRT}{100}$$

> in algebra you can leave out the '×'sign

where I is the interest,
        P is the money invested the 'principal',
        R is the present interest rate p.a.,
        T is the time in years.

In Martyn's case $P = 600$, $R = 4$, $T = 2$:

$$I = \frac{600 \times 4 \times 2}{100} = 48$$

Martyn's simple interest over 2 years is £48.

How much simple interest would Martyn earn over 5 years?

1 Work out the simple interest on each of these.

a) £500 at 6% p.a. for 1 year

b) £4000 at 5% p.a. for 3 years

c) £200 at 3% p.a. for 2 years

d) £5000 at 7% p.a. for 4 years

e) £1500 at 4% p.a. for 2 years

f) £4500 at 7.5% p.a. for 5 years

2 Work out the simple interest on each of these amounts using the interest rates in the table.

Amount	Interest rate
up to £100	1% p.a.
£100–£999	4% p.a.
£1000–£4999	4.5% p.a.
£5000 and over	5% p.a.

a) Edward invests £700 for 3 years.

b) Frances invests £8500 for 2 years.

c) Jack invests £3000 for 4 years.

d) Zoe invests £80 for 1 year.

Building societies and banks compete with each other. They offer you different rates of interest on your savings. This rate depends on the amount you have to invest and whether you want to be able to take out your money without giving advance notice. (This is called *instant access.*)

Go to at least one building society or bank.

Find out the rates they offer on instant access accounts.

Compare your information with others in your group.

What is the highest rate of interest you can get on £200?

What is the highest rate you can get on £500, £1000 and £5000?

For each amount, work out the highest amount of simple interest it could earn in 2 years.

Finishing off

> **Now that you have finished this chapter you should be able to**
>
> ★ work out wages
>
> ★ work out monthly earnings and salaries
>
> ★ use salary scales
>
> ★ work out commission
>
> ★ work out simple interest

Use the questions in the next exercise to check that you understand everything.

Mixed exercise

1 What is the weekly wage of

a) Hassan who works a 5-day week and is paid £70 a day?

b) Abigail who earns £5.50 an hour and works a 37-hour week?

2 Emma's normal rate of pay is £5 an hour. She works 4 hours' overtime at 'double time'.

How much does she earn?

3 Steven works 36 hours a week and is paid £8.50 an hour. He also does 2 hours' overtime which is paid at 'time and a half'. Find his total wage for the week.

4 Here is Kevin's time sheet for last week. Copy it and complete the last column.

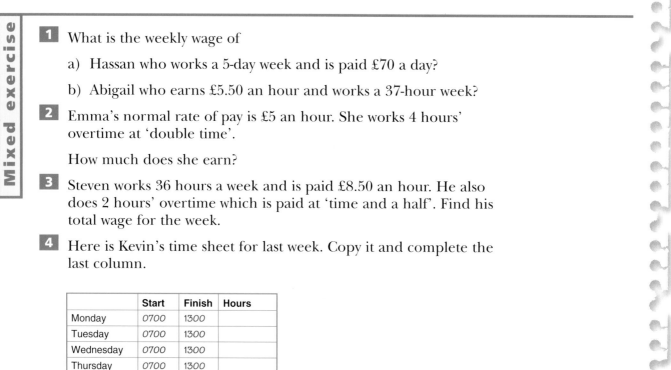

	Start	Finish	Hours
Monday	0700	1300	
Tuesday	0700	1300	
Wednesday	0700	1300	
Thursday	0700	1300	
Friday	0700	1300	
Saturday	0800	1300	
Sunday	0900	1300	
		Total	

From Monday to Saturday Kevin is paid £6 an hour. On Sunday he is paid 'double time'.

How much did Kevin earn last week?

5 a) Caroline's salary is £12 864 a year. How much does she earn in a month?

b) Matthew earns £350 a month. How much does he earn in a year?

6 Meena gets a job as a building inspector and starts on point 2 of this salary scale.

Her salary goes up one point after each year with the company.

a) What is her starting salary?

b) What is her salary after $1\frac{1}{2}$ years?

c) What is her salary after $3\frac{1}{2}$ years?

Point	Salary (£)
1	14 200
2	14 650
3	15 100
4	15 550
5	16 000

7 Mick earns £800 a month plus commission. His commission is 20% of the value of the goods he sells.

These are Mick's sales figures for the first 3 months of the year.

Month	January	February	March
Sales	£1000	£1500	£1200

Work out Mick's total pay for
a) January   b) February   c) March
d) the whole 3-month period.

8 Katie invests £300 at 4% p.a. for 2 years. How much simple interest will she get?

9 Alice and Jack both want to open an account at a building society.

They are offered these rates.

Amount	Interest rate
up to £999	3% p.a.
£1000–£2499	4% p.a.
£2500 and over	5% p.a.

Alice has £900 and Jack has £1600. They both want to invest their money for 3 years.

a) How much simple interest will Alice get?

b) How much simple interest will Jack get?

c) How much extra money would they get by investing their £2500 in a single account?

Collect 8 advertisements for the types of job that interest you.

What is the highest pay you have found?

What is the lowest you have found?

Why do you think some advertisements do not give a rate of pay?

Would you take a job 5 minutes' walk from home, or a similar job 20 miles away worth £2000 a year more?

Explain your answer.

Nineteen

Estimation

Approximations

Abigail is driving to a job interview.
She finds herself in a traffic jam.
A radio bulletin says that the traffic jam is 8 miles long.

Does this mean that it is exactly 8 miles long?

Very often, numbers that you read or hear are **approximations**.

The radio report means that the traffic jam is approximately 8 miles long.
It means they think that 8 is the nearest whole number.
The traffic jam might be 7.7 miles long, or 8.4 miles.

This number line shows the range of numbers that can be described as
'approximately 8' or 'about 8'.

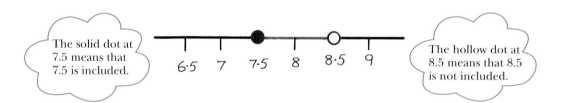

The solid dot at
7.5 means that
7.5 is included.

6·5   7   7·5   8   8·5   9

The hollow dot at
8.5 means that 8.5
is not included.

What is the nearest whole number to 7.5?

Usually, a number ending in .5 is rounded up to the next whole
number. So 7.5 is rounded up to 8, and 8.5 is rounded up to 9.

*A traffic jam is 5.2 miles long. What would the radio bulletin call this,
to the nearest whole number?*

Abigail drove about 600 miles in her car last month.
This figure is rounded to the nearest 100.

Look at this number line. It shows the range of numbers that can be
described as 'about 600'.

500   550   600   650   700

What is the smallest number of miles that can be described as 'about 900'?

What is the greatest number of miles that can be described as 'about 900'?

1 a) Write 56.8 seconds to the nearest second.

b) Write £64.23 to the nearest pound.

c) Write 241 miles to the nearest 10 miles.

d) Write 77 km/h to the nearest 10 km/h.

e) Write 575 kilocalories to the nearest 100 kilocalories.

f) Write 2368 m^2 to the nearest 100 m^2.

g) Write £26 788 to the nearest £1000.

h) Write 0.753 to the nearest whole number.

2 Estimate

a) the number of hours you have been alive,

b) the length of time you have spent asleep,

c) the number of times your heart has beaten today,

d) the number of meals you have eaten,

e) the weight of food you have eaten.

Investigation

Measure your height in centimetres.

Write it to the nearest centimetre.

Write it to the nearest 10 cm.

Write it to the nearest metre.

Collect 8 newspaper articles that include some approximation statements.

Examples: They played to a crowd of 30 000.

The bullet missed by a fraction of an inch.

For each statement, give the range of numbers that you think it might mean.

Is the meaning always clear?

Abigail is in an 8-mile-long traffic jam on the motorway. There are 3 lanes on the motorway.

a) Estimate how many vehicles are involved.

b) Estimate how many people are involved.

Estimating costs

Vicky buys these clothes.

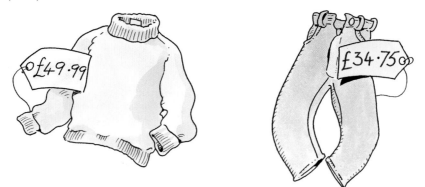

Vicky does not want to be overcharged so she makes a rough estimate of the total cost.

£49·99 is about £50
£34·75 is about £35
£50 + £35 = £85

Work out the exact cost.

Is Vicky's estimate close to it?

Dean and his two brothers go to a Pizza Bar. They each order a pizza costing £5.95, and Dean orders an ice cream costing £2.10.

The waitress gives Dean a bill for £23.95.

Dean is surprised by the amount so he makes a rough estimate.

£5·95 is about £6
3 pizzas cost about
3 × £6 = £18
£2·10 is about £2
so whole bill including
ice cream is about
£18 + £2 = £20

Do you think the bill was correct?

Work out the exact cost of 3 pizzas and an ice cream.

1 Use this menu to estimate the cost of each of these meals.

(Write down the cost of each item to the nearest pound, then add them up.)

a) Andrew has steak pie and chips.

b) Clare has chicken, chips and a large juice.

c) Marcus has plaice, chips and ice cream.

d) Emily has cod, chips, a cream cake and a small juice.

MENU

Chicken £2·90	Ice cream £1·90
Cod £2·85	Cream Cake £2·85
Plaice £2·95	Juice (small) £1·10
Steak Pie £1·85	Juice (large) £2·10
Chips £1·10	

2 Estimate the total cost of these purchases.

a)

b)

MILK SHAKES 99p each

c)
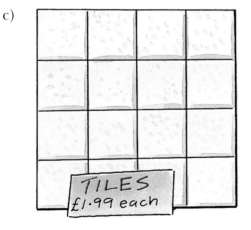

TILES £1·99 each

d)
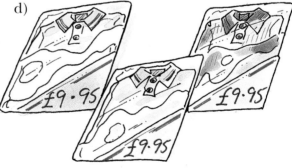

£9·95   £9·95   £9·95

3 Mel's weekly rent is £49.

Estimate how much rent she pays in a year.

You start your first job next month in an office.

Estimate the cost of buying a new set of clothes.

Rough calculations

This map shows the distances in miles between 6 factories owned by a company.

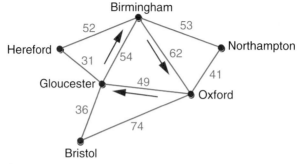

Ben works at the Oxford factory.

He has fixed up a day of meetings so he has to travel the route shown by the red arrows.

He writes down the distances.

Oxford ⟶ Gloucester	49
Gloucester ⟶ Birmingham	54
Birmingham ⟶ Oxford	62

Ben estimates the total distance.

Describe how Ben worked this out.

Work out the exact distance of Ben's trip.

Was his estimate close to the exact answer?

Ben's car can travel 38 miles on a gallon of petrol. How many gallons of petrol does he need?

Ben does this rough calculation.

Do you think Ben will have enough petrol if he has 4 gallons?

1 Use the map on the opposite page.

For each of these drivers, round each part of their journey to the nearest 10 miles. Add them up to get an estimate of the total distance.

a) Graham drives from Hereford to Gloucester and back.

b) Carmel drives from Birmingham to Northampton, on to Oxford and back to Birmingham.

c) Ahmed drives from Bristol to Birmingham and back by the shortest route.

2 Estimate how many gallons of petrol each of these drivers uses.

a) Steve drives 197 miles. (His car does 42 miles per gallon.)

b) Lisa drives 243 miles. (Her car does 32 miles per gallon.)

3 Write down each length to the nearest 10 metres, then estimate the area of the rectangle.

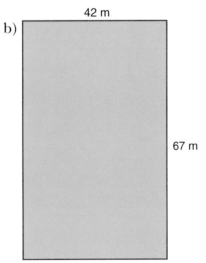

b)

42 m

67 m

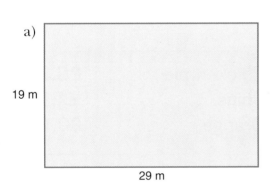

a)

19 m

29 m

4 For each of the rectangles in question 3, work out the exact area.

Compare the result with your estimate.

5 Nina is doing an 8.2 miles long walk.

She walks the first mile in 19 minutes.

Estimate how long the whole walk will take.

You can buy potatoes in 25 kg sacks.

Estimate how many potatoes there are in 1 sack.

Finishing off

> **Now that you have finished this chapter you should be able to**
>
> ★ approximate to the nearest whole number, nearest 10, nearest 100 and so on
>
> ★ estimate prices to the nearest pound
>
> ★ estimate total costs
>
> ★ make rough calculations

Use the questions in the next exercise to check that you understand everything.

Mixed exercise

1 a) Write £17.85 to the nearest pound.

b) Write 83 minutes to the nearest 10 minutes.

c) Write 3826 to the nearest 100.

d) Write 63 883 to the nearest 1000.

2 Tony buys one CD that costs £7.75 and another that costs £11.15.

Estimate the total cost to the nearest pound.

3 Paul is given this bill after he has eaten in a cafe.

a) Write down the price of each item to the nearest pound.

b) What is your rough estimate of the bill?

c) Should Paul pay the £6.85?

Chicken pie	£3.85
Chips	£1.05
Orange	£0.95
Total	£6.85

4 A school play is held in the hall.

There are 12 rows of chairs with 18 chairs in each row.

a) Estimate the number of chairs in the hall.

Tickets cost £3 each and the hall is nearly full.

b) Estimate the total receipts.

5 Ebrahim drives 241 miles.

His car does 31 miles per gallon.

a) Estimate the number of gallons used.

The journey takes 4 hours.

b) Estimate his average speed in miles per hour.

6 Forest Park is open to visitors from May until September. This table shows the number of visitors last year.

Month	May	June	July	August	September
Number of visitors	7780	8200	12 130	13 840	6319

a) Write each figure to the nearest thousand.

b) Use these figures to estimate the total number of visitors.

c) The entry fee was £2.95. Estimate the total receipts.

7 For each of these rectangles write down each length to the nearest 10 cm.

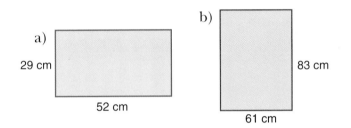

a) 29 cm 52 cm

b) 83 cm 61 cm

Use your rounded numbers to estimate the perimeter of the rectangles.

8 For each of the rectangles in question 7, work out the exact perimeter.

Compare this result with your estimate.

Estimate the number of words in a typical paperback novel.

Using what you know already, estimate the cost of

a)   a wedding reception,

b)   a youth hostelling trip, 1 week long,

c)   feeding yourself for 1 week,

d)   re-furnishing your bedroom,

e)   buying and running a car.

Choose one of these to cost more accurately.

Find the exact and up-to-date costs from brochures, catalogues or showrooms, etc.

Add up the costs to get a more accurate figure.

Twenty

Probability

Calculating probabilities

Katijah is playing snakes and ladders.

She is on square 21 and throws a single die.

How likely is she to land on square 25, which has a ladder?

To land on square 25, Katijah must throw a 4.

When she throws the die there are six possible outcomes: 1, 2, 3, 4, 5 or 6. They are all equally likely.

In everyday English you say

> 6 because there are six equally likely outcomes.

> 1 because there is just one way of getting a 4.

'There is a 1 in 6 chance of getting a 4.'

In mathematics you say

'The probability of getting a 4 is $\frac{1}{6}$.'

> short for probability

You can write this as $P(4) = \frac{1}{6}$

Here are two other examples of calculating probabilities.

Tossing a fair coin:

> 1 head

$P\,(\text{head}) = \frac{1}{2}$

> 2 sides

Choosing a card at random from a pack:

$P\,(\text{ace}) = \frac{4}{52} = \frac{1}{13}$

> 4 aces

> 52 cards

? *What do the words 'fair' and 'random' mean when you are talking about tossing a coin or choosing a playing card?*

Probability is a number on a scale between 0 (impossible) and 1 (certain).

It can be written as a fraction, a decimal or a percentage, so a probability of $\frac{1}{2}$ can also be written as 0.5 or 50%.

> This is a probability line

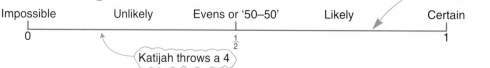

Impossible	Unlikely	Evens or '50–50'	Likely	Certain
0		$\frac{1}{2}$		1

Katijah throws a 4

176

1 You throw a dice. What is the probability that you get

   a) a 6?   b) an even number?   c) an odd number?

2 A fish is caught at random from this tank. What is the probability that it is

   a) red?

   b) blue?

   c) green?

3 What is the probability that the next light that fails on this Christmas tree will be

   a) yellow?

   b) pink?

   c) blue?

   d) red?

4 The diagram shows a game of draughts.

   At random red picks one of the pieces that can move.

   What is the probability that it can be taken, when he moves it?

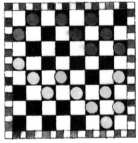

5 2 out of the 32 teeth in Arthur's mouth are bad; the rest are good.

   He goes to an incompetent dentist who pulls out a tooth at random.

   What is the probability that the tooth pulled out is

   a) bad?

   b) good?

The balls used in the National Lottery are numbered 1, 2, . . . up to 49.

At the draw, 7 of them are selected at random (6 balls and 1 bonus ball).

What is the probability that a particular ball will be selected in the draw?

Find out the outcomes of a large number of recent draws (at least 35).

Do your results suggest that some balls are luckier than others?

Do you believe that they are?

Working with probabilities

At a fête Tim chooses a number on the Wheel of Fortune.

If his number ends up at the bottom he wins a prize.

He chooses number 7.

What is the probability that Tim wins a prize?

> **There are 10 equally likely numbers. Tim chooses 1 of them.**
>
> **The probability that he wins is $\frac{1}{10}$.**

You can also work out the probability that Tim does not win.

There are 9 non-winning numbers, so the probability that he does not win is $\frac{9}{10}$.

You will notice that

$$P\text{ (Tim wins)} \quad + \quad P\text{ (Tim does not win)} = \quad 1$$
$$\frac{1}{10} \quad + \quad \frac{9}{10} \quad = \quad 1$$

If you add the probabilities of all the possible outcomes the answer always comes to 1.

Tim plays 20 times. How many prizes does he expect to win?

Tim expects to win 1 in every 10 times.

He plays 20 times so he expects to win

$$\frac{1}{10} \times 20 = 2 \text{ times}$$

That does not mean he always wins exactly twice every 20 times.

Sometimes he wins more than that (and we say he is lucky), sometimes fewer.

Fairground games are not always fair.

What could be done to make the Wheel of Fortune unfair?

1 Bella is playing Scrabble.

These 20 tiles are in the bag and she chooses one without looking.

What is the probability that she chooses:

a) the letter A?

b) a tile which scores 1 point?

c) a tile which scores more than 1 point?

d) a tile which scores 5 points?

e) a tile which is not an N?

2 In a raffle 400 tickets have been sold. Alex has bought 5 of them.

The tickets are put in a hat and one is selected for first prize.

What is the probability that

a) Alex wins first prize?

b) Alex does not win first prize?

In fact Ron wins first prize. His ticket is not put back.

Another ticket is now drawn for second prize.

c) What is the probability that Alex wins second prize?

3 In a gambling game you buy a scratch ticket for 50p.

Out of every 40 tickets, one is marked WINNER – COLLECT £15, the others LOSER – TRY AGAIN.

a) What is the probability that a ticket is a winner?

b) What is the probability that a ticket is a loser?

Hamish buys 2 tickets a week for 60 weeks.

c) How many tickets does Hamish buy, and how much do they cost?

d) How many of Hamish's tickets can he expect to be winners?

e) How much money can he expect to win?

f) What is his profit or loss? Explain your answer.

g) Do you think that if Hamish goes on playing he will end up making a profit?

Make a circular spinner like the Wheel of Fortune on the opposite page but design it to be unfair.
Test it and see if it really is unfair.

Estimating probabilities

In many situations you cannot calculate probability exactly, but you can sometimes estimate it using past data.

What is the probability that you will be ill next Tuesday?

When James was asked this question he looked at his diary for last year. He found 4 days when he was ill.

| 19 and 20 January | 1 March | 10 August |
| Heavy cold | Cough | Sunstroke |

There is no exact answer to this question but James's data does allow him to make an estimate:

$$\text{Probability of being ill one day} = \frac{\text{number of days ill}}{\text{total number of days}} = \frac{4}{365} = 0.01096$$

Because this is only an estimate it is better to give the answer rounded: about 0.01 (or 1%).

You can only estimate probability well if all the possible outcomes are equally likely.

- *Are you more likely to be ill on some days than others?*

- *Can you do anything to change your probability of being ill?*

  Decide which of the following will decrease the probability of your being ill, which will increase it and which will have no effect.

Have plenty of sleep	Eat fruit and vegetables
Eat junk food	Smoke
Take exercise	Drink heavily
Miss breakfast	Laugh and have fun

Although estimating probability may not be exact, it is very important for some people.

Why do the following people need to estimate probabilities?

- *Insurance company managers*

- *Bookmakers (bookies)*

1 June drives across a major junction on her way to work every day.

She notes that, out of 20 days, the traffic lights are green on 6 days and red on the rest.

Estimate the probability that next time she will find the lights
a) green   b) red.

2 In a survey of 7000 children, 1004 were found to be left handed.

A baby is about to be born.

Estimate the probability that the baby is
a) left handed   b) not left handed.

Give your answers as fractions with the numbers rounded sensibly.

3 Roy plants a packet of 40 seeds. They all grow into plants.

10 of these plants have pink flowers, the rest white.

Next year Roy plants 5 similar packets.
a) Estimate the probability that a seed chosen at random from these will grow into a pink-flowering plant.
b) About how many of the seeds would Roy expect to grow into plants with pink flowers?
c) Estimate the probability that a seed chosen at random will grow into a white-flowering plant.
d) About how many of the seeds would Roy expect to grow into plants with white flowers?

4 Last year there was no rain in Avonford on 30 out of 90 days in January, February and March.

a) Estimate the probability that it will rain on 6 March next year.
b) Estimate the probability that it will not rain on 6 March next year.
c) Do you trust your answers?

5 Ela keeps a record of how many letters she receives each day (except Sunday) for 10 weeks and then draws this line chart.

Use Ela's data to estimate the probability that on Thursday next week she will receive
a) 1 letter   b) 3 letters
c) 3, 4 or 5 letters   d) 12 letters.
Do you believe your answer to part d)?

Solitaire is a well known card game that you can play on many computers.
Play enough games for it to come out completely several times and so estimate the probability that this happens.

Finishing off

Now that you have finished this chapter you should be able to

★ when possible calculate the probability of an outcome using theory

★ calculate the probability of an outcome not happening

★ use probability to estimate the number of times an outcome will occur

★ use past data to estimate probability

Use the questions in the next exercise to check that you understand everything.

Mixed exercise

1 Draw a probability line and mark on it points A, B, C, D, E to show the probabilities that

A A cat will catch a mouse somewhere today
B You will live to the age of 145 years
C When you toss a coin it will come down heads
D A football match, selected at random, will end in a draw
E You will see the sun on Friday next week

2 A playing card is chosen at random from an ordinary pack of 52.

What is the probability that it is
a) a diamond?
b) a red card?
c) a queen?
d) the queen of diamonds?

3 There are 28 dominoes in a standard set. This one is 2-4.

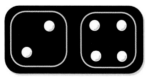

Either list or draw the full set of dominoes.

You choose a domino at random from the complete set. What is the probability that

a) it has a 6 on it?
b) it is a double?
c) the two numbers on it are different?

4 Two children play a game with dice. Tan throws a red die and then Lim throws a green die.

The one with the higher score is the winner.
If the two dice have the same score, the game is a draw.

In one game Tan throws a 3. What is the probability that

a) Lim wins?
b) Tan wins?
c) The game is drawn?

Add your three answers together.
d) What do you notice?
In the next game Tan throws a 6.
e) What is the probability of Lim winning?

5 Kevin is the supervisor on a production line making mugs. Yesterday he noticed that 15 out of 500 mugs were chipped and so were rejected.
   a) Estimate the probability that any mug made today will chipped.
   b) Estimate the probability that any mug made today will not be chipped.
   c) The company makes 50 000 mugs one day. How many of these would Kevin expect to be chipped?

6 The police do a survey of 100 motorists going under a particular bridge over a motorway, using a speed camera.

Speed (mph)	under 60	60–69	70–79	80–89	90+
Number of cars	8	28	34	26	4

They use these data to estimate the probability that a car chosen at random will be doing a certain speed.

Find the probability that a randomly selected car is travelling at
a) under 60 mph   b) under 80 mph   c) 80 mph or over.

They decide to prosecute all those doing 90 mph or over.
During one afternoon 12 000 cars go by.
d) Estimate how many of them will be prosecuted.

You could do this as a computer simulation, or as an experiment in a group.

Are dice always fair?

Throw a die 6 times and record the results on a tally.

Each of the 6 numbers, 1, 2 …6, could come up once but you may well find that one or two numbers come up more than once and others not at all.

Now throw the die 60 times and show your results on a line chart.

Are all the lines exactly the same height?

Use your results to estimate the probability of each possible outcome 1, 2 …6.

The theoretical answers are $\frac{1}{6}$ (or about 0.167) each.

How close are your answers to this?

Now do this as a group, each throwing a die 60 times, and put all your results together.

Are your estimated probabilities closer to $\frac{1}{6}$ now?

Twenty one

Moving shapes

Reflection and rotation

You can reflect a shape drawn on a square grid in either the *x* axis or the *y* axis.

The reflection must be the same distance from the mirror line as the original shape.

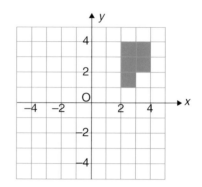

Reflection in the *x* axis

Reflection in the *y* axis

You can also rotate the shape about the origin, O.

The rotated shape must be the same distance from O as the original shape.

Rotation through $\frac{1}{4}$ turn clockwise

Rotation through $\frac{1}{2}$ turn

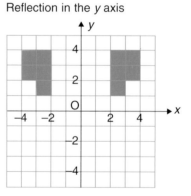

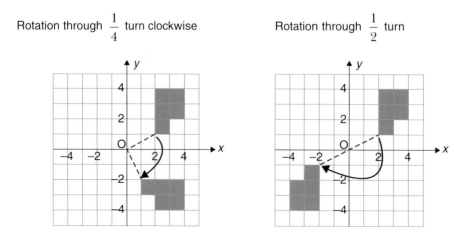

You may find it helpful to draw the shape on tracing paper and keep a finger at the origin.

Moving shapes

1 a) Copy these grids and the shapes on them onto squared paper.

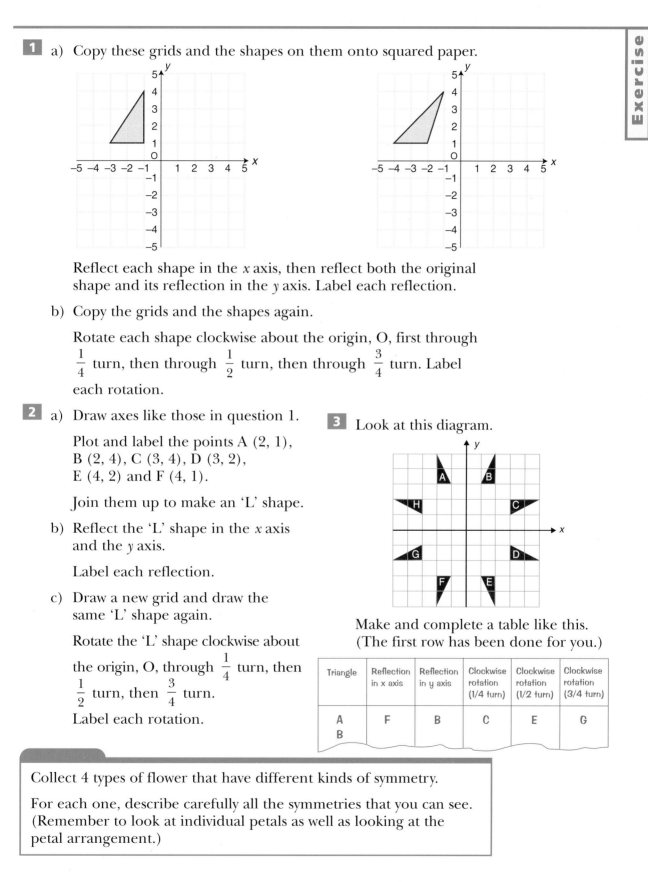

Reflect each shape in the *x* axis, then reflect both the original shape and its reflection in the *y* axis. Label each reflection.

b) Copy the grids and the shapes again.

Rotate each shape clockwise about the origin, O, first through $\frac{1}{4}$ turn, then through $\frac{1}{2}$ turn, then through $\frac{3}{4}$ turn. Label each rotation.

2 a) Draw axes like those in question 1.

Plot and label the points A (2, 1), B (2, 4), C (3, 4), D (3, 2), E (4, 2) and F (4, 1).

Join them up to make an 'L' shape.

b) Reflect the 'L' shape in the *x* axis and the *y* axis.

Label each reflection.

c) Draw a new grid and draw the same 'L' shape again.

Rotate the 'L' shape clockwise about the origin, O, through $\frac{1}{4}$ turn, then $\frac{1}{2}$ turn, then $\frac{3}{4}$ turn.

Label each rotation.

3 Look at this diagram.

Make and complete a table like this. (The first row has been done for you.)

Triangle	Reflection in x axis	Reflection in y axis	Clockwise rotation (1/4 turn)	Clockwise rotation (1/2 turn)	Clockwise rotation (3/4 turn)
A	F	B	C	E	G
B					

Collect 4 types of flower that have different kinds of symmetry.

For each one, describe carefully all the symmetries that you can see. (Remember to look at individual petals as well as looking at the petal arrangement.)

Translation

Meena is using a computer drawing program to design wrapping paper.

First she draws the picture she wants to use for the design.

Then she moves the cursor and copies the picture at different positions on the page.

This is Meena's first picture

For these pictures, Meena moves the cursor down the same distance each time

For each picture in this row, Meena moves the cursor the same distance to the right

The copies of the drawing are examples of **translations**.

The diagram below shows a shape being translated on a grid.

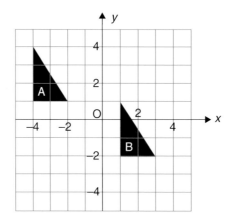

Shape A is translated 5 squares to the right and 3 squares down to make B.

To make shape B into shape A you need a translation of 5 squares to the left and 3 squares up.

You now know 3 different ways of moving shapes – reflection, rotation and translation.

• Reflection turns the shape over, or 'flips' it.

• Rotation turns the shape round.

• Translation moves the shape without turning it over or round.

Moving shapes

1 Describe the translations
   a) from A to B
   b) from B to A
   c) from A to C
   d) from A to D
   e) from B to D
   f) from C to D
   g) from B to C.

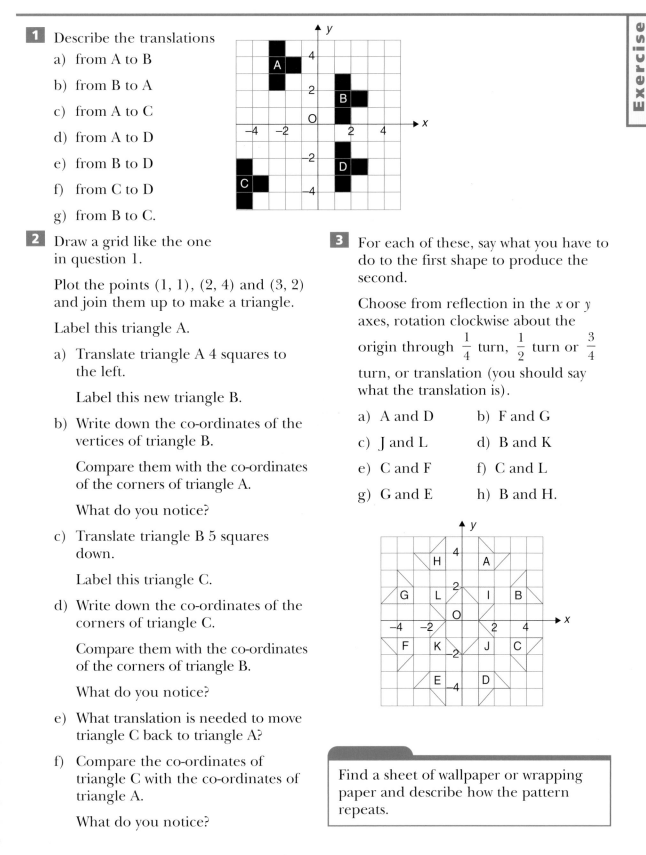

2 Draw a grid like the one in question 1.

Plot the points (1, 1), (2, 4) and (3, 2) and join them up to make a triangle.

Label this triangle A.

   a) Translate triangle A 4 squares to the left.

   Label this new triangle B.

   b) Write down the co-ordinates of the vertices of triangle B.

   Compare them with the co-ordinates of the corners of triangle A.

   What do you notice?

   c) Translate triangle B 5 squares down.

   Label this triangle C.

   d) Write down the co-ordinates of the corners of triangle C.

   Compare them with the co-ordinates of the corners of triangle B.

   What do you notice?

   e) What translation is needed to move triangle C back to triangle A?

   f) Compare the co-ordinates of triangle C with the co-ordinates of triangle A.

   What do you notice?

3 For each of these, say what you have to do to the first shape to produce the second.

Choose from reflection in the *x* or *y* axes, rotation clockwise about the origin through $\frac{1}{4}$ turn, $\frac{1}{2}$ turn or $\frac{3}{4}$ turn, or translation (you should say what the translation is).

   a) A and D   b) F and G
   c) J and L   d) B and K
   e) C and F   f) C and L
   g) G and E   h) B and H.

Find a sheet of wallpaper or wrapping paper and describe how the pattern repeats.

Enlargement

Look at these two photographs.

The right hand one is an **enlargement** of the left hand one.

The enlargement is twice as long and twice as high as the original photograph.

The length and height of the original photograph have been multiplied by 2 to get the length and height of the enlargement.

We say that it is an enlargement with **scale factor 2**.

This cannot be an enlargement of the same photograph. Although it is twice as high as the original photograph, it is more than twice as long. In an enlargement, all the lengths must be multiplied by the same scale factor.

Drawing enlargements

To draw an enlargement, you multiply the lengths of all the lines by the scale factor.

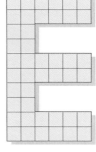

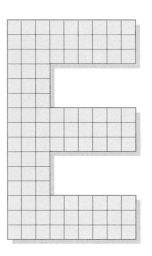

1 Which of these shapes are enlargements of A?

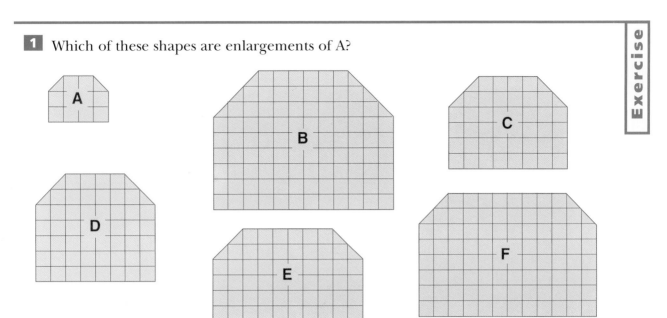

2 For each of the following letters of the alphabet

   a) copy the drawing on squared paper

   b) draw an enlargement with scale factor 2

   c) draw an enlargement with scale factor 3.

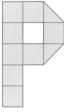  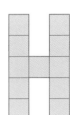 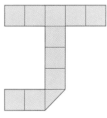

3 You can enlarge a drawing that does not have straight lines by using squared paper.

The picture on the right is drawn on a half-centimetre grid.

Copy it square-by-square onto a sheet of centimetre squared paper.

By what scale factor have you enlarged it?

Trace the outline of a country or island from an atlas.

Enlarge it to fill, as nearly as possible, a sheet of A4 paper.

Using a centre of enlargement

Look at these patterns of 8 enlarging squares.

In each case, starting from the smallest square,

- the second square is an enlargement with scale factor 2
- the third square is an enlargement with scale factor 3
- and so on.

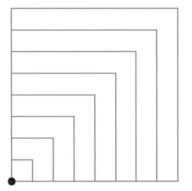
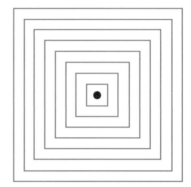

Both patterns are made of the same squares.

They look different because their **centres of enlargement** are different. These are shown by dots on the patterns.

The centre of enlargement is the point from which you start the enlargement.

In an enlargement with scale factor 2, every point on the enlargement is twice as far from the centre of enlargement as it was in the original.

Example

Enlarge this shape by a scale factor of 3 using C as the centre of enlargement.

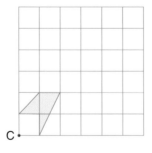

Solution

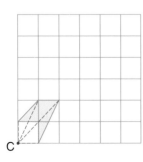
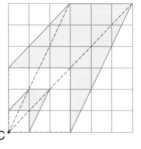

Where is the centre of enlargement in this child's toy?

Is each piece a true enlargement?

1 Copy these diagrams on squared paper.

Enlarge each shape by a scale of 2, using the point C as the centre of enlargement.

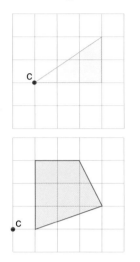

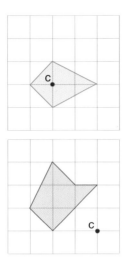

2 Copy these diagrams on squared paper.

Enlarge each shape by a scale factor of 3, using the point C as the centre of enlargement.

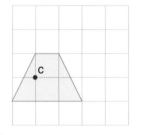

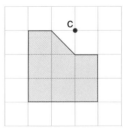

3 Copy this diagram on squared paper, but make both your axes go from 0 to 12.

a) Make enlargements with scale factors 2, 3 and 4, with the origin as the centre of enlargement.

b) Write down the co-ordinates of each corner of the original shape and of your three enlargements.

c) Compare the co-ordinates of each enlargement with those of the original shape.

What do you notice?

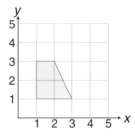

Find a photo that you like.

Choose part of the photo to enlarge to fit a standard frame 17 cm by 11.5 cm.

Make it clear for the enlarger which part of the photo you want.

Finishing off

★ draw the reflection of a shape in the *x* axis or the *y* axis

★ rotate a shape about a point through $\frac{1}{4}$ turn, $\frac{1}{2}$ turn or $\frac{3}{4}$ turn

★ carry out and describe a translation of a shape

★ recognise and draw an enlargement of a simple shape using a whole number scale factor

★ recognise and draw an enlargement of a simple shape using a whole number scale factor and a centre of enlargement

Use the questions in the next exercise to check that you understand everything.

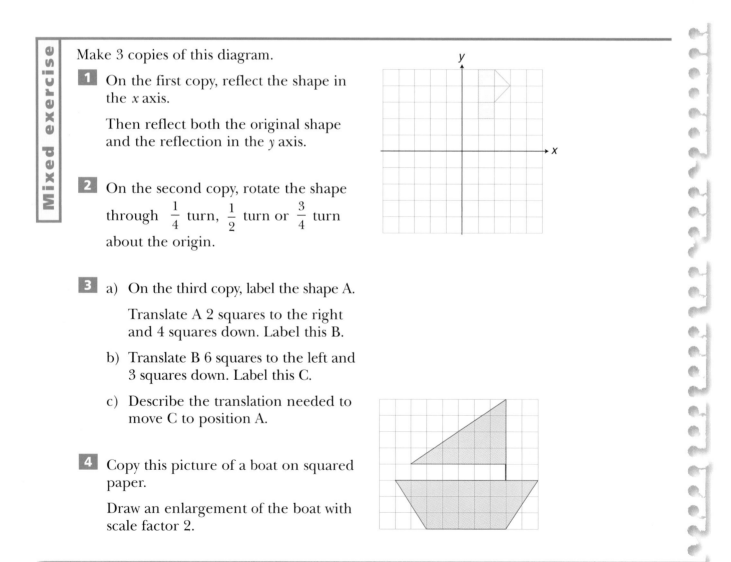

Mixed exercise

Make 3 copies of this diagram.

1 On the first copy, reflect the shape in the *x* axis.

Then reflect both the original shape and the reflection in the *y* axis.

2 On the second copy, rotate the shape through $\frac{1}{4}$ turn, $\frac{1}{2}$ turn or $\frac{3}{4}$ turn about the origin.

3 a) On the third copy, label the shape A.

Translate A 2 squares to the right and 4 squares down. Label this B.

b) Translate B 6 squares to the left and 3 squares down. Label this C.

c) Describe the translation needed to move C to position A.

4 Copy this picture of a boat on squared paper.

Draw an enlargement of the boat with scale factor 2.

5 Which of these triangles is an enlargement of triangle A?

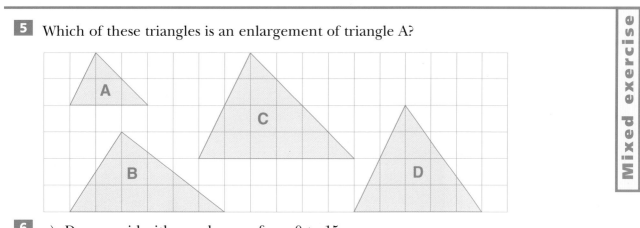

6 a) Draw a grid with *x* and *y* axes from 0 to 15.

Plot the points (2, 1), (2, 3), (3, 3), (4, 1) and join them up.

b) Make an enlargement with scale factor 3, using the origin as the centre of enlargement.

Investigation

The 'L' shape on the right is an enlargement with scale factor 2 of the 'L' shape on the left.

Four of the original 'L' shapes can be fitted into the enlargement.

a) Draw enlargements of the original 'L' shape with different scale factors.

Investigate how many of the original 'L' shapes can be fitted into each enlargement. (They must fit exactly with no gaps.)

b) Find a rule linking the scale factor and the number of the original 'L' shapes that fit into an enlargement.

Look at an up-and-over garage door and see how it works.

Make any measurements you will need.

Make a scale drawing of the door, viewed from the side, in several positions from fully closed to fully open.

Where is it safe to stand?

Answers

Chapter 1: Co-ordinates

Page 5: Finding a square

1 a) D2   b) A3   c) F3
2 a) B4   b) E3   c) E4   d) D4, E4

Page 7: Finding a point

1 (7,8)
2 (6,2) (7,2) (8,2) (9,2)
3 1 m   **4** 1 m long, $\frac{1}{2}$ m wide
5 a) (10,20) b) (50,19) c) (30,32) d) (35,28)
6 a) 10 km b) 20 km c) 30 km

Page 9: Mathematical co-ordinates

1 The Plough (2,4), (3,7), (6,8), (9,9), (11,7), (15,8),
            (15,12)
    Orion   (6,3), (6,7), (4,14), (9,13), (8,9), (7,8),
                 (11,4)
2 Ask your teacher to check your constellations.
3 Square of side 2 units
4 Join (2,1) to (3,3) to (2,4) to (1,3) to (2,1)

Chapter 2: Using numbers

Page 13: Length

1 a) 200   b) 400   **2** a) 5000   b) 8000
3 a) 30   b) 90   **4** a) 2   b) 3.5 $(3\frac{1}{2})$
5 a) 76 miles   b) 138 miles
    c) Southampton to Brighton
6 a) 60 m   b) 100 m   **7** Yes (with 6 cm to spare)
8 Width 13 cm, depth 8 cm

Page 15: Weight and mass

1 a) 1000 g   b) 0.5 kg   c) 2000 ml   d) 4 pints
2 a) 20 kg   b) 2   c) 2000   d) 5000
3 122
4 a) No (375 kg)   b) No (305 kg)   c) Yes (295 kg)
5 a) 5   b) 25   **6** a) 28   b) 7

Page 17: Time

1 a) 2 hours b) 1 minute 30 seconds
2 a) 180 seconds   b) 75 minutes
3 3 minutes 25 seconds
4 a) 0435   b) 1740   c) 2120   d) 1350
5 a) 8.25 am   b) 2.30 pm   c) 11.45 pm   d) 6.15 pm
6 a) 53   b) Yes   c) No
7 a) 30 minutes ($\frac{1}{2}$ hour) b) 10 minutes
    c) Tennis Highlights   d) 35 minutes
8 a) 0845   b) 0915

Page 19: Money

1 £9   **2** £1   **3** £156   **4** £820   **5** £246   **6** £898
7 £845   **8** £1080   **9** Golden Sands: cheaper by £27

Chapter 3: Types of number

Page 23: Types of number

1 a) 13, 21, 47   b) 8, 36, 44
    c) Even numbers end with a multiple of 2, i.e.
       0, 2, 4, 6 or 8.
    d) 3
2 a) 10   b) 15   c) 20   **3** 9
4 a)

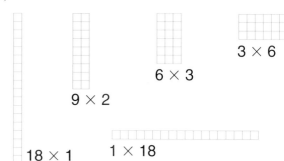

    b) Factors of 18 are 1, 2, 3, 6, 9 and 18.
5 a) 3   b) 2
6 a) 1, 2, 5, 10   b) 1, 2, 4, 8, 16
    c) 1, 7   d) 1, 2, 4, 5, 10, 20
    e) 1, 3, 5, 15   f) 1, 2, 3, 5, 6, 10, 15, 30
    g) 1, 2, 7, 14   h) 1, 3, 7, 21
    i) 1, 2, 3, 4, 6, 8, 12, 16, 24, 48
    j) 1, 2, 3, 6, 9, 18, 27, 54   k) 1, 2, 4, 7, 14, 28
    l) 1, 2, 3, 4, 5, 6, 10, 12, 15, 20, 30, 60

Page 25: Prime numbers

1 a) No   b) Yes   c) No   d) Yes
    e) No   f) No   g) Yes   h) No

Page 27: Squares, square roots and cubes

1 a) 25   b) 64   c) 81   d) 144   e) 400
2 a) 5   b) 7   c) 10   d) 11   e) 20
3 8
4 a) 64   b) 81   c) 10   d) Yes, 11 along each side.
5 a) 27   b) 64   c) 125

Chapter 4: Symmetry

Page 31: Reflection symmetry

1 B, C and D
2 a) 2   b) 4   c) 6
   d) 1   e) 3   f) 2
3 a) Many possibilities: ask your teacher to check
       your patterns.
   b) Many possibilities: ask your teacher to check
       your patterns.
   c) Many possibilities: ask your teacher to check
       your patterns.

Page 33: Drawing reflections

Ask your teacher to check your drawings.

Page 35: Rotational symmetry

1 A and D
2 a) 2   b) 4   c) 3
   d) 8   e) 6   f) 4
3 Ask your teacher to check your drawings.

Chapter 5: Fractions

Page 39: Equivalent fractions

1 $\frac{1}{3}$ 2 $\frac{3}{5}$ 3 a) $\frac{5}{8}$ b) $\frac{3}{8}$

4 a) $\frac{13}{16}$ b) $\frac{12}{16} = \frac{3}{4}$ c) $\frac{25}{32}$

5 $\frac{2}{4}, \frac{3}{6}, \frac{4}{8}$ (and many other possibilities)

6 a) $\frac{1}{2}$ b) $\frac{3}{4}$ c) $\frac{3}{8}$

   d) $\frac{1}{3}$ e) $\frac{2}{3}$ f) $\frac{1}{5}$

   g) $\frac{3}{4}$ h) $\frac{1}{5}$ i) $\frac{1}{4}$ j) $\frac{5}{7}$

Page 41: Adding and subtracting fractions (1)

1 a) $\frac{1}{2}$ b) $\frac{3}{4}$ c) $\frac{1}{4}$ d) $\frac{5}{8}$

   e) 1   f) $\frac{1}{8}$ g) 1   h) $\frac{1}{4}$

2 a) $\frac{5}{8}$ b) $\frac{3}{8}$

3 a) $\frac{1}{4} + \frac{3}{4} = 1$ b) $\frac{2}{3} + \frac{1}{3} = 1$ c) $\frac{3}{8} + \frac{5}{8} = 1$

4 a) 10   b) $\frac{5}{12}$ c) $\frac{1}{4}$ d) $\frac{3}{4}$ e) $\frac{13}{24}$ f) $\frac{11}{24}$

5 a) $\frac{3}{4}$ b) $\frac{5}{8}$ c) $\frac{9}{10}$ d) $\frac{1}{4}$

   e) $\frac{13}{16}$ f) $\frac{3}{10}$ g) $\frac{1}{2}$ h) $\frac{3}{8}$

Page 43: Adding and subtracting fractions (2)

1 a) 2   b) 2   c) 4   d) 3
   e) 3   f) 3   g) 12   h) 3
   i) 4   j) 14   k) 5   l) 30

2 a) $\frac{3}{4}$ mile   b) $\frac{3}{8}$ mile   c) $\frac{5}{8}$ mile   d) $\frac{7}{8}$ mile

3 a) $\frac{3}{8}''$ b) $\frac{5}{8}''$ c) $\frac{11}{16}''$ d) $\frac{7}{16}''$

4 a) $\frac{5}{16}$ b) $\frac{10}{16} = \frac{5}{8}$ c) $\frac{7}{8}$ d) $\frac{5}{8}$

   e) $\frac{13}{16}$ f) $\frac{5}{8}$ g) $\frac{11}{16}$ h) $\frac{11}{8} = 1\frac{3}{8}$

Page 45: Improper fractions and mixed numbers

1 a) $1\frac{1}{4}$ b) $2\frac{2}{3}$ c) $1\frac{1}{2}$ d) $2\frac{3}{4}$

   e) $1\frac{5}{8}$ f) $4\frac{1}{2}$ g) $1\frac{5}{6}$ h) 4

2 a) $\frac{7}{2}$ b) $\frac{13}{8}$ c) $\frac{13}{5}$ d) $\frac{10}{3}$

   e) $\frac{19}{4}$ f) $\frac{19}{16}$ g) $\frac{21}{8}$ h) $\frac{25}{4}$

3 $3\frac{1}{2}$ 4 $3\frac{1}{4}$ 5 6   6 5   7 11   8 18   9 21

Page 47: Mixed numbers

1 a) $4\frac{1}{4}$ b) $2\frac{1}{2}$ c) $1\frac{3}{8}$

   d) $4\frac{3}{8}$ e) $1\frac{5}{16}$ f) $2\frac{3}{8}$

   g) $1\frac{3}{4}$ h) $2\frac{3}{4}$ i) $2\frac{5}{8}$

2 a) 3 miles   b) $3\frac{3}{4}$ miles

   c) $3\frac{1}{2}$ miles   d) $7\frac{1}{4}$ miles

3 $3\frac{1}{4}$ hours   4 $1\frac{1}{2}$ kg   5 $1\frac{1}{4}$ hours

6 a) $4\frac{1}{4}''$ b) $1\frac{1}{4}''$

Page 49: Fractions of a quantity

1 a) 6   b) 6   c) 40
   d) 9   e) 72   f) 40
2 £20   3 6   4 a) £3   b) £9
5 a) £8000   b) £15 000
6 a) 16 cm   b) 12 cm   7 £800 000   8 20

Chapter 6: Maps and drawings

Page 53: Maps and scales

1. a) Green family   b) Pub or station
   c) School   d) White family
2. a) West   b) North-west
   c) South-west   d) South
3. North-east   4 Shop
5. Turn left out of the house. Walk to the end of the road and turn left. At the end of the road turn left. Take the first right, then the second right, and the station is on the left.
6. Turn left out of the station. Take the second right, first right, first left, first right, first left, and the hotel is on your right.
7. a) 7 cm (±0.5cm)
   b) 70 m (±5m)
8. a) Mark
   b) Jessica 17 cm, Mark 6 cm, Ryan 7 cm
   c) Jessica 170 m, Mark 60 m, Ryan 70 m

Page 55: Scales

1. a) 250 m   b) 1500 m   c) 200 m
   d) 75 m   e) 237.5 m
2. a) 2 cm   b) 100 000 cm   c) 1000 m   d) 1 km
3. a) 4 mm   b) 200 m
4. 56 mm on the map; 2.8 km in real life
5. Lounge: 7.5 m by 4.5 m
   Dining room: 3.75 m by 3.75 m
   Kitchen: 5.25 m by 2.25 m
   Cloakroom: 3.75 m by 2.25 m
   Bathroom: 3 m by 3 m
   Bedroom 1: 4.5 m by 3 m
   Bedroom 2: 3.75 m by 3 m
   Bedroom 3: 4.5 m by 3.75 m

Page 57: Angles

1. a) obtuse angle   b) acute angle   c) right angle
   d) acute angle   e) reflex angle   f) obtuse angle
3. a) 130°   b) 30°   c) 90°
   d) 65°   e) 330°   f) 110°
4. GO FORWARD 5 METRES
   TURN LEFT 45°

Chapter 7: Decimals

Page 61: Tenths and hundredths

1. A: 3.2   B: 3.5   C: 3.9
2. a) 5.4   b) 2.48   c) 4.13
3. a) $\frac{7}{10}$ b) $\frac{31}{100}$ c) $\frac{4}{10} = \frac{2}{5}$ d) $\frac{45}{100} = \frac{9}{20}$
   e) $2\frac{9}{10}$ f) $3\frac{14}{100} = 3\frac{7}{50}$ g) $4\frac{641}{1000}$ h) $\frac{9}{100}$

4. a) 0.9   b) 0.71   c) 0.3   d) 0.28
   e) 2.7   f) 4.23   g) 3.1   h) 1.37
5. A: £1.1m   B: £0.7m   C: £1.6m
   D: £0.4m   E: £2.4m

Page 63: Halves and quarters

1. a) 2.25   b) 3.5   c) 5.75   d) 1.5
   e) 3.75   f) 7.25   g) 6.5   h) 1.75
   i) 0.8   j) 1.6   k) 3.2   l) 2.4
2. a) $4\frac{1}{2}$ b) $3\frac{1}{4}$ c) $2\frac{3}{4}$ d) $8\frac{1}{2}$
   e) $1\frac{1}{4}$ f) $5\frac{1}{2}$ g) $4\frac{3}{4}$ h) $6\frac{1}{4}$
   i) $\frac{3}{5}$ j) $1\frac{2}{5}$ k) $2\frac{4}{5}$ l) $3\frac{1}{5}$
3. A: 4.5   B: 4.25   C: 4.75

4.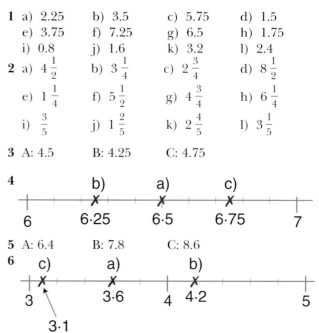

5. A: 6.4   B: 7.8   C: 8.6
6.

Page 65: Adding and subtracting decimals

1. a) £3.55   b) £8.90   c) £6.15
   d) £8.10   e) £0.12   f) £2.95
2. a) 4.8   b) 7.92   c) 21.03
   d) 1.89   e) 0.21   f) 1.71
3. £3.01   4 £10.35   5 1.45 km   6 0.7 m (70 cm)

Page 67: Multiples of 10

1. a) 16   b) 30.1   c) 210
   d) 35   e) 760   f) 3.2
2. 150
3. a) £2.40   b) £24.00   4 £50 000   5 £350.00
6. a) 7.01   b) 0.73   c) 0.06
   d) 6.32   e) 0.826   f) 0.00611
7. £7   8 £24.50   9 1.5 m
10. a) £4.50   b) £3.50   11 1.6 litres

Page 69: Multiplying decimals

1. a) 7.2   b) 6.0   c) 8.88   d) 0.8
   e) 0.12   f) 7.28   g) 0.062   h) 95.4
2.

Name	Height at age 2 (m)	Fully grown height (m)
Amy	0.85	1.70
Jack	0.83	1.66
Ryan	0.96	1.92
Laura	0.89	1.78

3 Guiseley→Bingley: 4.8 miles
   Bingley→Keighley: 3.0 miles
   Keighley→Silsden: 4.2 miles
   Silsden→Addingham: 3.6 miles
   Addingham→Ilkley: 2.4 miles
   Ilkley→Guiseley: 5.4 miles
4 a) £3.50   b) £8.75
   c) Yes: 10 sessions would normally cost £17.50.
5 a) 2.25   b) 4.84   c) 0.25   d) 23.04
6 a) 900   b) 249   c) 350   d) 10 000
   e) 10 000   f) 18   g) 20   h) 5050
7 £270 000

Page 71: Dividing decimals

1 a) 8.1   b) 70.1   c) 0.661
   d) 0.28   e) 2300   f) 1.3
2 a) £0.55 (55p) b) £1.98 c) £0.74 (74p)
3 £32.97   4 £3.60   5 1.75 m   6 £48
7 72p (£0.72)
8 No
9 a) 600   b) 15   c) 25
   d) 1000   e) 1.5   f) 1600
10 a) 2.5   b) 1.8   c) 2.8   d) 4.3   e) 7.2

Chapter 8: Shapes

Page 75: Sorting shapes

1 a) 3 sides (triangles)   b) 4 sides (quadrilaterals)
   c) 5 sides (pentagons)   d) 6 sides (hexagons)
   e) 8 sides (octagons)
   f) All sides are the same length and all angles are equal (regular shapes).
2 a) E, M, V   b) B, D, H, P, R, V
   c) B, C, F, I, J, K, L, N, Q, S, T, W, X
   d) A, C, K   e) B, F, H, N, Q, R, T, V, X
   f) F, H, J, N, Q, U

Page 77: Triangles

1 a) F   b) E   c) B   d) A
   e) G   f) D   g) C
2 FCA, FHC, FGE and EHG are right-angled scalene triangles.
   FDA, ADB and DGE are acute-angled scalene triangles.
   FHE is an obtuse-angled isosceles triangle
   DCB, ADC and FGD are obtuse-angled scalene triangles
   AFG is a right-angled isosceles triangle
   CEH is an acute-angled isosceles triangle

Page 79: Quadrilaterals

1 The number of lines of symmetry for each shape are:
   a) 4   b) 2   c) 2
   d) none   e) 1   f) none or 1
2 Many possible answers: ask your teacher to check your drawings.
3 a) T   b) F   c) F
   d) T   e) F   f) T

Page 81: Other kinds of shapes

1 a)

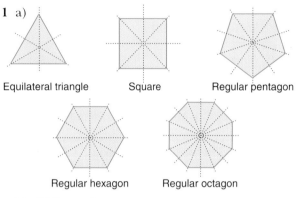

Equilateral triangle   Square   Regular pentagon

Regular hexagon   Regular octagon

   b) 50 lines of symmetry
2 C, F and G

Page 83: Circles

1 Clock faces, jam jar lids, drilled holes, buttons, camera lenses, saucers, and many others.
2 Ask your teacher to check your circles.
   c) (radius should be 3.5 cm)
3 a) about 25 cm   b) about 34 cm   c) about 22 cm

Chapter 9: Percentages

Page 87: 25%, 50% and 75%

1

Fraction	Decimal	Percentage
$\frac{1}{4}$	0.25	25%
$\frac{1}{2}$	0.5	50%
$\frac{3}{4}$	0.75	75%

2 C   3 A   4 B   5 C   6 C

Page 89: Finding percentages

1 a) 30%   b) 20%   c) 50%
2 a) 40%   b) 20%   c) 10%
3 a) 16%   b) 80%   c) 4%
4 a) Border 64%; Octo 24%; Tapestry 28%.
   b) Border $\frac{16}{25}$; Octo $\frac{6}{25}$; Tapestry $\frac{7}{25}$.
   c) Border 0.64; Octo 0.24; Tapestry 0.28.

Page 91: Percentage calculations

1 a) 300   b) 120   c) 140
    d) 72   e) 10   f) 135
    g) 2   h) 2   i) 60
    j) 22   k) 100   l) 16

2 £900

3 a) £360   b) £840   c) £1440

4 24   **5** £160   **6** £360   **7** £212   **8** £245

Chapter 10: Statistics

Page 95: Recording data

1 a)

Type of food	Fish & chips	Indian	Chinese	Pub meal
Frequency	1	11	2	6

   b) Indian   c) Yes. There are 20 tallies.

2 a)

Ride	Dragon's Tail	Splashdown	Pirate Plank	Octopus
Frequency	12	7	8	3

   b) 30   c) Dragon's Tail

Page 97: Displaying data

1 a)+b)

No. of days	Tally (a)	Frequency (b)
0 days	ⅢⅢ	5
1 day	ⅢⅢ ⅢⅢ	10
2 days	ⅢⅢ 1	6
3 days	1111	4
4 days	11	2
5 days		0
6 days		0
7 days	111	3

   c) 30
   d)

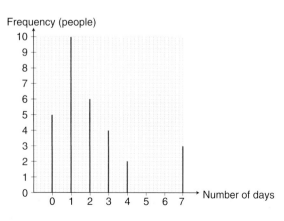

Frequency (people) vs Number of days

e) More of the runners go out every day, or nearly every day, in Summer, probably because of better weather or longer daylight hours.

2 a)

Reaction	Play	Friendly sniff	No reaction	Growl	Fight
Frequency	6	9	5	4	1

   b) 25   c) 20%

   d) Not really – each dog's behaviour must depend to some extent on the reaction of the other dog.

Page 99: Pie charts

1 a) 10%

   c) Liberal Alliance: 108°
      Christian Democrats: 72°
      Don't vote: 36°

   d) Ask your teacher to check your pie chart.

2 b) Greyhounds 72°; Bowling 144°; Skating 36°; Pub 18°.

   c) Ask your teacher to check your pie chart.

3 a) 6°   c) 25   d) 15   e) 90

Page 101: Grouping data

1 Ask your teacher to check your answer.

2 a)+b)

Age	Tally (a)	Frequency (b)
10–19	ⅢⅢ 111	8
20–29	1111	4
30–39	ⅢⅢ	5
40–49	ⅢⅢ 1111	9
50–59	1111	4
60–69	111	3
70–79	11	2

   c) They look short of people in the 20–40 age range, but they have quite a lot of teenagers.

3 a)+b)

Time	Tally (a)	Frequency (b)
12.0–12.9	111	3
13.0–13.9	111	3
14.0–14.9	ⅢⅢ 11	7
15.0–15.9	ⅢⅢ 1	6
16.0–16.9	ⅢⅢ 11	7
17.0–17.9	1	1
18.0–18.9	111	3

c) Frequency (people)

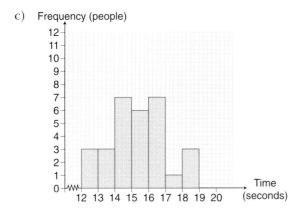

d) The world record for 100 m is under 10 seconds. Most of these times (24 out of 50) are between 14 and 20 seconds. They are not particularly fast. Perhaps the students are quite young, or they do not exercise regularly.

Page 103: Other data displays

1 a) Weight (kg)

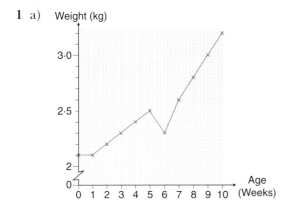

b) Week 6 (he lost weight)   c) 3.1 kg
2 a) 26
b) The fastest runners were those of middle weight: about 60–90 kg. The heaviest students tended to be very slow.

Page 105: Averages and spread

1 a) Mean 3; Median 2; Mode 1.
b) Mean 30; Median 20; Mode 10.
c) Mean 13; Median 12; Mode 11.
d) Mean 103; Median 102; Mode 101.
2 a) Mean 4.9; Median 5; Mode 6.
b) It will be full about 1 time in 10.
3 a) Mean 12 hours; median 12.5 hours; mode 5 hours; range 23 hours.
b) Mean 11 hours; median 11 hours; no mode. The mean and the median are both higher for the boys than for the girls, so the boys watch more TV than the girls.

4 a) Mean 13 s; median 13 s; mode 11 s; range 5 s.
b) Mean 13 s; median 12 s; mode 11 s; range 7 s. The PE staff are perhaps slightly faster: their mean time is the same as the students but their median time is 1 s less. However they are less consistent, with one very slow member.
5 a) Mean £15 667 (to nearest £1); median £11 000; mode £8000.
b) £65 000

Chapter 11: Directed numbers

Page 109: Negative numbers

1 a) Up 1   b) Down 1   c) Down 3
d) Down 2   e) Up 4   f) Down 3
2 a) £100   b) –£100   c) £0
3 a) £20   b) –£5 (i.e. £5 loss)
4 a) Down 250 m   b) Up 200 m   c) Down 300 m
d) Up 350 m

Page 111: Adding and subtracting

1 a) 4   b) –4   c) –6   d) 1
e) 7   f) –7   g) 3   h) –3
i) 3   j) –3   k) 7   l) –7
2 a) –1   b) 100   c) –20   d) –1000
3 London 4 °C; Manchester –1 °C; Leeds –3 °C; Inverness –6 °C; Accra 30 °C.
4 a) –2 ft   b) 0.5 ft   c) 3 ft   d) 1.5 ft

Chapter 13: Algebra

Page 119: Making connections

1 60p
2 1→ 70   3 1→ 30
   2→140   2→ 60
   3→210   3→ 90
   4→280   4→120
   5→350
   6→420
   7→490
   8→560
   9→630
  10→700
4 Potatoes   Apples   Bananas
  1→0.20   1→0.50   1→0.40
  2→0.40   2→1.00   2→0.80
  3→0.60   3→1.50   3→1.20
  4→0.80   4→2.00   4→1.60
  5→1.00   5→2.50   5→2.00

5 a)
1→2.50	11→27.50
2→5.00	12→30.00
3→7.50	13→32.50
4→10.00	14→35.00
5→12.50	15→37.50
6→15.00	16→40.00
7→17.50	17→42.50
8→20.00	18→45.00
9→22.50	19→47.50
10→25.00	20→50.00

b) £45.00

Page 121: Finding a formula

1 a) To find the price in £ you multiply the weight by 0.2.
b) $P = 0.2 \times W$
c) $P = 0.2 \times 12 = 2.4$, so 12 kg costs £2.40.

2 a)
x	y		A	B
1→	3		1→	4
2→	6		2→	5
3→	9		3→	6
4→	12		4→	7
5→	15		5→	8
6→	18		6→	9
7→	21		7→	10
8→	24		8→	11
9→	27		9→	12
10→	30		10→	13

3 a) 300 pence b) 720 pence c) 10 litres
d) 30 litres   e) $P = 70 \times L$

Page 123: Conversion graphs

1 a) $16 b) $40 c) $80 d) $128
2 a) £20 b) £30 c) £90 d) £100
3 a) £10 b) 18
4 Ask your teacher to check your graph.

Chapter 14: Travel graphs

Page 127: Distance and time

1 5 minutes
2 50 minutes
3 22.5 minutes (The first 6 miles took 15 minutes and the last 3 miles took 7.5 minutes.)
4 10.45 am
5 120 km
6 a) 1 hr 45 mins   b) 30 mins
7 Ask your teacher to check your graph.

Page 129: Finding the speed from a travel graph

1 0930
2 a) 5 km   b) 1 hr   c) 5 km/h
3 a) 7 km   b) 1 hr 45 min c) 4 km/h
4 4 km/h

Page 131: Drawing travel graphs

1 a) Won't fit   b) Yes
c) Yes   d) Ask your teacher to check your graph.
e) 8.11 am (to nearest minute) and 8.25 am.
2 a) Ask your teacher to check your graph.
b) 4 mph   c) 30 mph

Chapter 15: Spending money

Page 135: Bills

1 159   **2** 271   **3** 60p   **4** 72p   **5** 224p (£2.24)
6 480p (£4.80)   **7** £53   **8** £38.50
9 a) 400   b) 8000p = £80   c) £96
10 a) 663   b) £99.45   c) £141.45

Page 137: Buy now , pay later

1 a) £192   b) £42   **2** a) £840   b) £190
3 a) £384   b) £84   **4** a) £648   b) £148
5 £208   **6** £65
7 a) £50   b) £1800   **8** a) £550   b) £6600

Page 139: Value added tax (VAT)

1 a) £21   b) £141   **2** a) £31.50 b) £211.50
3 a) £14   b) £94   **4** a) £157.50 b) £1057.50
5 Store A, by £4.50
6 Store X, by £2.37 (to nearest penny)

Chapter 16: Perimeter and area

Page 143: Perimeter

1 a) 18 cm   b) 23 cm
2 a) 22 cm   b) 38 cm   c) 38 cm   d) 44 cm
3 £3695.20

Page 145: Area

1 a) 35 cm^2 b) 55 cm^2 c) 32 cm^2 d) 55 cm^2
2 a) 29 cm^2 b) 35 cm^2 **3** a) 35 cm^2 b) 48 cm^2

Page 147: Area of a rectangle

1 a) Area: 63 cm^2; Perimeter 32 cm
b) Area: 60 cm^2; Perimeter 34 cm
c) Area: 66 m^2; Perimeter 34 m
d) Area: 10 m^2; Perimeter 13 m
2 a) 14 cm^2 b) 27 cm^2 c) 20 cm^2
d) 33 cm^2 e) 14.5 cm^2 f) 38 cm^2

Chapter 17: Three dimensions

Page 151: Drawing solid objects

R and X go with A (cuboid).
S and Y go with B (cylinder).
P and Z go with C (pyramid).
Q and W go with D (cone).

Page 153: Using isometric paper

Ask your teacher to check your drawings for questions 1 and 2.

2 a) 9   b) 11   c) 22   d) 19

Page 155: Nets

1 A, D
2 Ask your teacher to check your net.
3 a) Pyramid b) 5   c) 8   d) 5
4 a) Triangular prism
     b) 5   c) 9   d) 6

Page 157: Volume

1 a) 120 m^3 b) 72 m^3 c) 60 m^3 d) 84 m^3
2 a) 48 cm^3 b) 30 cm^3 c) 18 cm^3 d) 42 cm^3

Chapter 18: Earning money

Page 161: Wages

1 a) £180   b) £90   c) £200   d) £120
2 a) 12   b) £60
3 a) 4   b) 21   c) £84
4 £48   **5** £33.75   **6** £312   **7** £215

Page 163: Salaries

1 £750   **2** £9840   **3** £400   **4** Sacha, by £780.
5 a) £8400   b) £9200   c) £10 000
6 May £850, June £875, July £840, August £765.
7 a) £14 000 b) £13 250

Page 165: Simple interest

1 a) £30   b) £600   c) £12
    d) £1400   e) £120   f) £1687.50
2 a) £84   b) £850   c) £540   d) 80p

Chapter 19: Estimation

Page 169: Approximations

1 a) 57 s   b) £64   c) 240 miles   d) 80 km/h
    e) 600 kcal   f) 2400 m^2 g) £27 000   h) 1
2 Check your answers with your teacher.

Page 171: Estimating costs

1 a) £3   b) £6   c) £6   d) £8
2 a) £6   b) £4   c) £24   d) £30
3 £2500

Page 173: Rough calculations

1 a) 60 miles   b) 150 miles   c) 180 miles
2 a) 5   b) 8
3 a) 600 m^2 b) 2800 m^2
4 a) 551 m^2 b) 2814 m^2
5 160 minutes (2 hours 40 minutes)

Chapter 20: Probability

Page 177: Calculating probabilities

1 a) $\dfrac{1}{6}$ b) $\dfrac{3}{6} = \dfrac{1}{2}$ c) $\dfrac{3}{6} = \dfrac{1}{2}$

2 a) $\dfrac{7}{12}$ b) $\dfrac{3}{12} = \dfrac{1}{4}$ c) $\dfrac{2}{12} = \dfrac{1}{6}$

3 a) $\dfrac{5}{14}$ b) $\dfrac{3}{14}$ c) $\dfrac{2}{14} = \dfrac{1}{7}$ d) $\dfrac{4}{14} = \dfrac{2}{7}$

4 $\dfrac{3}{6} = \dfrac{1}{2}$

5 a) $\dfrac{2}{32} = \dfrac{1}{16}$ b) $\dfrac{30}{32} = \dfrac{15}{16}$

Page 179: Working with probabilities

1 a) $\dfrac{2}{20}\left(=\dfrac{1}{10}\right)$ b) $\dfrac{10}{20}\left(=\dfrac{1}{2}\right)$ c) $\dfrac{10}{20}\left(=\dfrac{1}{2}\right)$

    d) $\dfrac{2}{20}\left(=\dfrac{1}{10}\right)$ e) $\dfrac{18}{20}\left(=\dfrac{9}{10}\right)$

2 a) $\dfrac{5}{400}\left(=\dfrac{1}{80}\right)$ b) $\dfrac{395}{400}\left(=\dfrac{79}{80}\right)$ c) $\dfrac{5}{399}$

3 a) $\dfrac{1}{40}$ b) $\dfrac{39}{40}$ c) 120 tickets, £60
    d) 3   e) £45
    f) −£15 (The minus sign shows that it is a loss, not a profit.)
    g) No

Page 181: Estimating probabilities

1 a) $\frac{6}{20}\left(=\frac{3}{10}\right)$ b) $\frac{14}{20}\left(=\frac{7}{10}\right)$

2 a) $\frac{1}{7}$ b) $\frac{6}{7}$

3 a) $\frac{10}{40}\left(=\frac{1}{4}\right)$ b) 50 c) $\frac{30}{40}\left(=\frac{3}{4}\right)$ d) 150

4 a) $\frac{2}{3}$ b) $\frac{1}{3}$

  c) Not really, January probably had most of the rainy days.

5 a) $\frac{1}{3}$ b) $\frac{8}{60}\left(=\frac{2}{15}\right)$ c) $\frac{1}{4}$ d) 0

  Zero is probably a good approximation but it is not impossible that she'll get 12; it could be her birthday.

Chapter 21: Moving shapes

Page 185: Reflection and rotation

1 Ask your teacher to check your drawings.

2 Ask your teacher to check your drawings.

3

Triangle	Reflect. in *x* axis	Reflect. in *y* axis	C/wise rotation ($\frac{1}{4}$ turn)	C/wise rotation ($\frac{1}{2}$ turn)	C/wise rotation ($\frac{3}{4}$ turn)
A	F	B	C	E	G
B	E	A	D	F	H
C	D	H	E	G	A
D	C	G	F	H	B
E	B	F	G	A	C
F	A	E	H	B	D
G	H	D	A	C	E
H	G	C	B	D	F

Page 187: Translations

1 a) 4 squares to the right and 2 squares down

  b) 4 squares to the left and 2 squares up

  c) 2 squares to the left and 7 squares down

  d) 4 squares to the right and 6 squares down

  e) 4 squares down

  f) 6 squares to the right and 1 square up

  g) 6 squares to the left and 5 squares down

2 b) (–3, 1), (–2, 4), (–1, 2)

  The *x* co-ordinates of B are 4 less than the *x* co-ordinates of A.

  d) (–3, –4), (–2, –1), (–1, –3)

  The *y* co-ordinates of C are 5 less than the *y* co-ordinates of B.

  e) 4 squares to the right and 5 squares up.

  f) The *x* co-ordinates of A are 4 more than the *x* co-ordinates of C, and the *y* co-ordinates of A are 5 more than the *y* co-ordinates of C.

3 a) Reflection in the *x* axis

  b) Reflection in the *x* axis

  c) Rotation $\frac{1}{2}$ turn clockwise about the origin

  d) Translation 5 squares to the left and 3 squares down

  e) Reflection in the *y* axis

  f) Translation 5 squares to the left and 3 squares up

  g) Rotation $\frac{3}{4}$ turn clockwise about the origin

  h) Rotation $\frac{3}{4}$ turn clockwise about the origin

Page 189: Enlargement

1 B, C

2 Ask your teacher to check your enlargements.

3 Ask your teacher to check your enlargement. It should have a scale factor of 2.

Page 191: Using a centre of enlargement

1 Ask your teacher to check your enlargements.

2 Ask your teacher to check your enlargements.

3 b) Original shape: (1, 1), (3, 1), (1, 3), (2, 3)

  Scale factor 2: (2, 2), (6, 2), (2, 6), (4, 6)

  Scale factor 3: (3, 3), (9, 3), (3, 9), (6, 9)

  Scale factor 4: (4, 4), (12, 4), (4, 12), (8, 12)

  c) Each co-ordinate has been multiplied by the scale factor.

Index